Jan Kusmirek

# LIQUID SUNSHINE
## Vegetable Oils for Aromatherapy

Jan Kusmirek is one of the world's leading Aromatherapists. His creations are found in a number of skin care, spa, and Aromatherapy ranges around the world. His private practice grew into a consultancy that has taken Aromatherapy to new dimensions. Well known in the profession for his committee work, especially in legal and parliamentary affairs, he helped with the establishment and regulation of the Aromatherapy profession. A prolific writer on the subject, his many articles, published in numerous professional journals, have kept readers up to date with trends and the latest technical developments.

Qualified not only in Aromatherapy but also Medical Herbalism and Naturopathy, the author has a wide spectrum of practical experience to contribute. In the 1970's he was heavily involved in horticulture and agriculture, and knows plants from the ground up as well as having real experience with drying, milling, and expelling process equipment. Additionally, his work experience and commitment to Organic growing methods enabled him to work directly for the Soil Association as Marketing Manager during a critical time in its development.

This unique blend of experience, from green plant to massage, provides the author with a world of ideas and a unique understanding of the natural world. He is equally at home lecturing to Cosmetic scientists, Medical professionals and Perfumers as he is to student Aromatherapists of all kinds. He loves Nature, and especially aromatics.

# Jan Kusmirek

# LIQUID SUNSHINE

## Vegetable Oils
## for Aromatherapy

*LIQUID SUNSHINE – Vegetable Oils for Aromatherapy*

First published in 2002 by Floramicus

Cover photograph by Christoph Wilhelm/Telegraph Colour Library
Cover design, typesetting and illustrations by Dragon Design (www.dragon-design.org)
Typeset in Lingwood 9.8/15.8 pt

**ISBN 0-9543295-0-3**

Printed in Italy

# Contents

# *Acknowledgements*

This book would not have come into being without the help and encouragement of a number of people. I would especially like to thank those many Aromatherapists who have contributed ideas and views. In particular, thanks goes to Teddy Fearnhamm, one time Chairperson of the Aromatherapy Organisations Council, Sylvia Baker, Secretary of the Aromatherapy Trades Council and Jade Shutes, President of the US National Association of Holistic Aromatherapists. Dr. Vivian Lunny and Favre Armstrong for medical aspects. Susan Mears for pushing matters and patience. Mary Kelsey for typing up the original manuscript, and Jayne Bailey for keeping real work going whilst I toiled. Valerie Serrano for much of the research, and Alban Muller for his help and cooperation in lending much technical data. Ken Carlson for conversations about processing, and Linda Kusmirek for the weekends and holidays that got lost in the book! Photo credits to J. Bailey and R. Sainsbury.

# *Preface*

This book is for anyone interested in using natural vegetable oils in the home, clinic or salon. It is written from the perspective of Classical Aromatherapy™, as this method of therapy has developed the topical use of vegetable oils for well being and health as no other. Aromatherapists will find the text useful and supportive but you do not need to be a trained therapist to enjoy the book or reap benefits from vegetable oils. Vegetable oils are a sacred gift from Nature: use them and enjoy their benefits.

My knowledge of vegetable oils comes from practical experience. My first experience with these marvellous gifts from nature came when I learned to use them in Aromatherapy. My training in this discipline led me to call them 'Carrier Oils'. They were simply used to convey the precious, fragrant essential oils to the skin. This was a fundamental error. Vegetable oils are so much more, and they have a value equal to the more popular fragrant essential oils. Vegetable oils do not come from green cabbages or carrot root. The term is generic, an umbrella name for oils derived from natural sources such as seeds and nuts. The seed can come from a tree, like a coconut, or from a plant, like a Sunflower. They are all vegetable oils.

Essential oils, being concentrated extracts of aromatic and other volatile substances from the plant, are not generally used neat on the skin. Some, but not all, essential oils are quite irritating or drying to the skin. Hence the need to dilute them in something that 'carries' them, and itself is skin compatible, hence 'Carrier Oils'.

Commercially, essential oils are sometimes diluted in alcohol and related substances. These may then be used as 'frictions' or tonics for the skin. Perfumes and colognes follow the same principles, the difference between the two being only the dilution rate of the essential oils or perfume compound. Colognes may be diluted at around 4% in alcohol whereas perfume or parfum may contain as much as 20% concentrates.

Aromatherapy in Britain uses massage techniques in association with essential oils. Clearly alcohol is not a good medium for massage whereas oil is. Aromatherapists from the 'natural' school to which I belong do not usually use mineral oil. Mineral oil has many names. It is derived from the petro-chemical industry and is found as baby oil, petrolatum or as the trade name Vaseline. Mineral oil has its place. It is, for example, inert and does provide slippage, which is needed for massage. In extremes of cold temperature, it can provide a moisture-saving barrier. It should, however, be thought of in this way – an occlusive barrier. It is not so good at letting skin breathe; it does not work in synergy with the skin.

Aromatherapists are by training inclined to view vegetable oils only as 'carrier' oils. Little effective training has been given about their practical uses or applications beyond that simple action. For many years I have taken classes around the world where the truth of this statement has been all too obvious. Students and therapists alike, when confronted with questions like 'Why do you use Grapeseed Oil rather than Sweet Almond Oil?', answer very simply, the most common answer being 'Because it's cheaper' or 'That's what they used at my school'. This is not so surprising as the school often acts as the supplier or the seller of the materials used by the students. This incestuous relationship lends itself to the seller promoting the cheapest or most profitable materials. Good schools promote the best materials for the purpose of the application or therapy in mind, irrespective of source or price.

When my first articles on vegetable oils appeared in the Aromather-apy press, they were very quickly seized upon by educators and suppliers alike. They were seen as new ways of making money, and little information has been written since beyond the few basic facts I put forward. Hence the pop-ularity of the courses I have undertaken over the years. The course 'Vegetable

Oils in Practice' is always oversubscribed. Professional therapists in health care, well-being or beauty have come to learn the benefits of these rather special 'active ingredients' that are of so much value and from Nature. Not all vegetable oils are the same. They have different characteristics, values, and uses. They have in common the effect of providing slippage for massage and some common chemistry, but each oil seed offers far more.

What attempts there have been at promoting the value of vegetable oils have mainly come from the perspective of industrial chemistry. This is not so surprising as Aromatherapy itself stands accused of selling its soul to school-book chemistry. This has come about due to the meteoric rise in the popularity of Aromatherapy and its commercialisation at all levels. Schools in competition with one another had little to offer in the early days of training. Those that offered chemistry were seen as the real champions of the scientific medical approach. Likewise with vegetable oils. Few people in the industry had actually used them, so hiring an industrial chemist with a basic knowledge of fatty acids as a guest tutor seemed like a solution to scholastic leadership.

My experience with vegetable oils was twofold, firstly via my studies in nutritional aspects and then in skincare. This latter avenue occurred at the time of major cosmetic industry changes to more natural or skin compatible ranges. The numerous brands I worked with gave me ample opportunity to study the advantages and disadvantages of materials in practical work situations. I also worked with the pioneering company Fragrant Earth in the world of professional Aromatherapy. Their customers provided plenty of anecdotal evidence about the behavioural characteristics of different materials. In particular, it was their customers, the professional Aromatherapists, who provided so much information on the blending of oils. Not just essential oils to vegetable oils but the blending of different vegetable oils with each other to achieve desirable characteristics of touch and effect.

All people should be aware of the life supporting value of vegetable oils. They have sustained mankind for millennia providing not only cosmetic, medical and nutritional actions, but providing sources of physical light, spiritual action, and metaphor.

This work is about natural materials used in a Naturopathic way. Whilst chemistry is valued, this book is for those whose roots lie in the complementary or alternative worlds of health and beauty. It is for all those who love Nature and want to work with it. I value the intuitive approach to matters. I value the significance of touch in the handling of materials as much as I do the hard science.

For me, theory has to fit the facts of experience, the reality of performance. It is not what something should do scientifically. It is what it does with an individual in a given set of circumstances that counts. In reality, science is as much about guesswork as anything else. The intuitive approach allows for change and imaginative actions to achieve results. Too often orthodoxy is overly restrictive and dismissive of anything that challenges its ways.

Aromatherapy, even though lamed professionally by increasing legislation and professional centralisation, is still the largest advocate of the use of vegetable oils. Most of its advocates are women. The pioneers in Aromatherapy were women. I know because I was one of the first men to take up the profession. This feminine aspect should be valued as contributing an adventurous and caring approach to using Nature's treasures for the benefit of humankind. Aromatherapy, Carrier Oils, and Vegetable Oils are part of that natural tradition and should not be straightjacketed so as to become ineffectual. Let Biodiversity in Nature reign supreme.

# 1

# A New Look at Fats and Oils

Very few people are inspired by the mention of fats and oils. They are not topics of everyday conversation. The words have very negative associations. They bring to mind all the wrong images. Yet fats and oils are vital to life. They provide substance and form, protection and healing.

The word 'fat' applied to human beings, animals or food is considered very undesirable. It is equated with ugliness and a rotund shape no one would want. "Fat" has come to mean obesity, poor shape and health, a lack of fitness or even laziness. Oil implies greasiness, impurity. Oily skin and hair is often interpreted as poor hygiene, or even poverty or lack of care. Fatty foods are really out of fashion and are a big 'No' for our health. Both words need a new appraisal and correct context.

Think of some other words applied to fat and oil, adjectives, descriptions that have the same or similar meanings yet give better definitions or images. Succulent and plump are good words when applied to a chicken but are they appropriate for your lover or partner? The answer partly depends upon honesty. What do you prefer to cuddle or hold? Something hard or soft? Someone thin and bony or soft and meaty? The beauties of the past as seen in all the famous pictures have substance, plumpness, roundness, and form. Only in our time has emaciation been considered good shape!

Cream summons up pictures of yummy puddings, cakes or perhaps fruit, strawberries and cream. Milk has all the sublime meaning of wholesomeness and goodness – our very mother, nurturing and caring. Butter conjures up such things as crumpets and hot toast just oozing with mouth-watering tastes. Margarine and crumpets are just not the same despite the efforts to find new marketing names with more appeal!

All this should lead us to conclude that in the modern world our decisions are as much made on emotion as fact. Witness the nightly images on television. Desirable foods, many full of fats, contrasted with images of slim models. Shining hair that comes from natural oils is washed and denatured to reflect light a new way. These images are contradictions in themselves.

Fats and Oils should be looked at in a new way, one that is focused on their good points. We can acknowledge that they have a downside but what doesn't? Balance in all things, and moderation, is an old tenet but still holds true. "A little of what you fancy does you good" is probably what most of our grandmothers said. The saying holds true today as it encourages people to eat a wide variety of foods. Unfortunately many do not take moderation as part of the saying. Overindulgence is mostly at the root of problems associated with fats, not the product itself.

## Growing Up With Fats and Oils

My first encounter with fats and oils was no doubt Baby Oil alongside Talcum powder. The former, based upon mineral oil or petrolatum, is out of favour with many mums and the latter thought by some as no longer a good thing due to its propensity to harbour allergens and micro-organisms. Despite calamity howlers, and like the majority of people, I survived both.

I suppose we could add soap to the list of fats. I certainly encountered that. As a young baby being washed by my father, I wriggled, he grasped me more firmly, and presto, I shot from his arms landing on my head on the gas cooker! Soap is slippery. Not too many people seem to realise that soap is based upon fat. It can be derived from vegetable or animal sources. Those familiar with the story of Pinocchio will remember this was the ultimate destiny of the poor old donkeys. The finest soap today can still be made from tallow or animal fat.

As I was dropped on my head by my father due to a combination of wriggling and soap, who was to blame? Recent legislation from the European

Union under the aegis of Health and Safety seems to undermine the principles of personal responsibility or exaggerate the potential for harm or threat from everyday events, substances or things around us. Should soap be banned for its potential to cause an accident? This may sound absurd but as we review commonplace materials, especially those from Nature, you will find that many regulations or warnings are taken to a point that is best described as a nanny state system. True, Nature is not safe and it has a potential for harm, but Vegetable Oils are amongst the safest of Nature's materials to use. Individual reactions or accidents should not provide legislators with an excuse to ban or restrict the birthright of every human being to free access to the materials Nature provides. Education and information is the key. So read labels in a way that allows for such information sources to be biased.

My later recollections of fats and oils include regular visits to the grocer in the small Buckinghamshire town in which I lived. Here my mother bought our butter. Great yellow squares were cut down to size. Wooden butter pats were used to shape the pieces and I remember the sound as our quarter pound was slapped and patted to shape before being wrapped in greaseproof paper. I love butter to this day.

My grandmother, from farming stock, taught me to make butter from the milk we purchased. The milk was poured from the bottle into a special little screw top container and shaken and shaken until a white butter formed. She loved Danish unsalted butter whereas I preferred the salted New Zealand. Different breeds of cows gave milk with different tastes and the pasture and time of year added to the diversity of flavour. Guernsey, Ayrshire, South Devon, all places as well as breeds. Such a variety of tastes and colours. Different breads and butters were my childhood delight. Give me bread and good butter any day.

On occasion there was bread and dripping. I apparently needed this when I was ill to feed me up. Not my favourite at all but underneath the dripping there was a layer of jelly and that was really good. Does anyone remember dripping today? In an age of processed food such words have lost meaning to many young people. It is the fat that comes from meat when roasting and allowed to solidify. Do you say 'yuk'?

So passed my complete understanding of natural fat as a young person. Butter, I learned at school, was so plentiful in the Middle Ages that they used it as axle grease. Olive Oil was used by the Romans for lighting purposes, and tallow used in England for the same purpose.

What of margarine? It came in hard blocks, usually branded Stork, and was for poor people! Margarine was used for cooking by my mother because it was cheaper. Pastry was made with lard, and lard was used for making real chips. It was not really until the 1970's that vegetable oils entered my consciousness. The health of the nation became a topic of news.

Today supermarket shelves are laden with vegetable cooking oils. Not so many years ago things were very different. There were neither supermarkets nor masses of vegetable oils. In many ways supermarkets have ruined local choice and settled for the bland, but they did open up a wider variety of materials, if only offering a poor selection, choosing price over quality. One example of a new fashionable product was vegetable oil.

Vegetable oils were seen, in the 1960's and 1970's, as a product of the Continent. In the early 1960's they could be sought in Continental or Jewish delicatessens and specialist shops, but not usually elsewhere. The situation was similar with Yoghurt. It just could not be found in regular stores. Both were considered part of particular health diets or what we now would call 'food fads'. Most of these fads seemed to come from Switzerland, perhaps from specialist clinics. One of the oddest of these new foods was muesli or dried cereals with fruit and nuts!

In practical life vegetable oils and margarines just crept in. A big boost to margarine came with the softening process. A lump of cold Stork margarine or even butter was no easy thing to handle. So butter began to lose out only when margarine began to be spreadable. Spreadability, not health, was the driving force. The first brand that I remember was Blue Band which managed to capture a more sophisticated image than previous margarines which were considered a little low class, the new phrase being 'down-market'.

Thanks to my parents I had always been brought up with an open mind and a fairly radical view of health. Our family doctor was not only a registered general practitioner but also a homoeopathic doctor. One of the family's best friends qualified as an Osteopath in the late 1950's. So it was hardly surprising that I came to the study of alternative medicine. I use the term 'alternative' because that is how I saw things, an alternative to orthodoxy.

Alternative does not mean the same as complementary. Complementary medicine runs alongside the orthodox view, sometimes within the British National Health Service. In a way it is a form of integrated medicine that seeks to take the supposed best from alternative care and add it to orthodox medicine. It seems incredible now but being concerned about nutrition and diet during the 1950's and on into the 1960's was considered very cranky if not downright dangerous. Diet was then very alternative. The idea that you are what you eat was a long way from being clearly understood.

My training in dietary therapy and naturopathy brought me into contact with a variety of radical ideas about nutrition and health. Naturopathy is a philosophy underpinning many alternative and complementary medicines. I suppose its fundamentals lie in the idea that the body can generally heal itself from disease given good diet and conditions. It promotes methods of growing and cooking that maintains the vitality of the food source. Closely associated with the Organic movement, naturopathy maintains that there is a vital force or energising principle in Nature that can be transferred. Natural raw materials such as food should therefore be considered in light of this philosophical view as well as their orthodox chemical make up. I learned that like any other substance, fats and oils were good for you. Their downsides were just a matter of type and intake.

My work in skincare and cosmetics brought me to further views concerned with the use of oils and fats. In essence any cream used on the body or face is an emulsion of water and oil. Manufacturers had long used mineral oil or petrolatum, paraffin wax (a common household name being Vaseline) as the oil phase or portion of the emulsion. Mineral oil is inert; in other words it does not do much and is not active. This is good from the formulators' point of view because it does not cause problems; it does not go off or rancid for example. It is also relatively cheap to buy and being stable, cheap to handle. It does not do much for the skin, as we shall see, so was thought less likely to cause skin irritations and such like. It was a novel wonder: safe, inert and a product of major reproducible industry in a brave new world and mass market.

Mass consumerism was contrasted in the late 1960's and early 1970's with a new consumerism. It was the period of the rise of the individual and self-expression. (Wide choice and individual need was not easy in a period of mass production.) In addition, responsibility toward Nature was beginning to impact upon popular thinking.

This was fertile ground for the rise of 'Health Food' shops and a change in cosmetics and toiletries too. With the rise of the Body Shop, Nature was seen as the source of a host of goodies for the skin. The Company, in very clever marketing, never made any claims as to efficacy. Rather, they concentrated upon emotional association and imagery to sell the products. "Never mind whether it works, women in Africa or some other exotic sounding place use it so try it yourself", seemed to be the marketing watchword and why not, it was fun. Exotic vegetable oils became fashionable as additions to emulsions or just as themselves. Why, you could even put oil directly on your skin and it did some good! Shades of hippies, the Beatles, Woodstock and Patchouli.

The trouble for industrialists was that not only was there a new breed of consumer, but vegetable oils did not behave like safe old mineral oil in mass produced emulsions! Thought had to go into their use and more careful formulations had to be made. The public wanted Nature but Nature was not easy to handle in production.

In the 1980's the fashion for 'health' food was well under way. A quiet revolution had taken place with the maturing of the Sixties generation. Ex-hippies in suits were now setting the trend in many areas. The 'vibes' of the Sixties, at one extreme, were now computer chips, and at the other end of the scale, were healing crystals. Investors and older board members simply wanted to maximise profit from this maturing generation who were also instilling creative shopping habits into their own children, a new consumer generation. The supermarkets and processed food manufacturers began to go healthy – their version. We see similar happenings today with organics; standards slip as the mass marketers move in.

Vegetable oils became equated with healthy cooking and eating. The Wok replaced the deep fat fryer. The Mediterranean diet became not only fashionable but also healthy. When Freddie Laker put air travel on the affordable map, ordinary British and US citizens really began to see what variety the world ate and smeared on themselves to look and feel good. High on this list was oil. Exotic oils like Sesame to cook with, or Coconut Oil to make your skin glisten and feel silky, or Evening Primrose Oil that was good for your heart and PMT! What's more, 'Science' said it was good for you! Good old commerce had dragged the academics into the arena. Research grants were available and soon food technologists and bio-scientists were everywhere leaving the alternative pioneers well and truly marginalized. They were quite right to say you didn't need to wear sandals to eat bean sprouts and, if you ate them, enjoy them! That is providing that you seasoned them with some good oil dressing and spread your bread with polyunsaturated margarine. The age of polyunsaturated margarine led the way to a healthy slim body with a low cholesterol blood supply and healthy heart.

Only no one seemed to tell the Eskimos who, very irritatingly to Science and much to the delight of the alternatives, continued to be round, oily, happy and healthy (apologies to all slim line Native Americans of the North West but this is a generalisation). The story of fats and oils seems to have been oversimplified. As the British innovators with Evening Primrose Oil struggled with research and grant aid, the big boys moved in with the miracle of GLA that suddenly seemed good for everything and could be found in greater quantities in Borage Oil. (The marketers didn't like this name and settled for a translation of the German to Starflower, at the time causing me and others a long search to find out what the product really was.) Then Nestle found Blackcurrant Seed Oil to be even better, and so Ribena ( a blackcurrant cordial) found an ecological twist in using its own produce to further improve the health of the world.

World production of vegetable oils had reached 68 million metric tonnes in 1994. Yet only 15% of this incredible total goes to non-food production. Increasingly petrochemicals will be replaced by raw materials drawn from these vegetable, renewable and environmentally friendly resources.

## The Growth of Aromatherapy

So far in the discussion we have concentrated on foods and cosmetics, but the real growth areas are likely to be in detergents (surfactants) and lubricants. This is probably the reason behind the big interest in Genetically Modified oil-bearing crops. This technology, so well promoted in the UK, owes a lot to the fact that the US produces close to half the world's consumption of oil crops. Although we have concentrated on vegetable oils, animal fats still amount to around 20% of US production. Transgenic crops (GM) of soybean, rapeseed and canola have been released and plans are underway for jojoba, coconut and others. Vegetable oils are certainly part of world consciousness as well as its economy.

Into this arena came Aromatherapy. The nineties were the decade of Aromatherapy. I do not believe that the impact of the UK and its promotion of the use of essential oils and vegetable oils for health and beauty has been appreciated or understood. Aromatherapy has had an amazing impact in the English speaking world and the Far East. Yet it is hardly known in the heart-land of the European Union. There are obvious political reasons for this.

First let us consider what Aromatherapy is. This is no easy task as views differ and it has become an umbrella word encompassing a wide variety of treatments. Its popularity in the UK is born out by its appearance in every common soap opera on TV and on Radio. Both Coronation Street and East Enders have its exponents. Even the highly traditional Archers has its resident Aromatherapist. Billboard hoardings advertising tobacco have used the word and it has been used to advertise everything from coffee to detergent. We now have aromatherapy candles and room deodorisers, aromatherapy washing-up liquid and soap. It is a played out word and passing fashion. So what is it really? How did it begin? What relationship does it have to vegetable oils?

Aromatherapy as practised in the UK is essentially an oil massage using essential oils diluted into a vegetable oil base. This is far from the whole story but you can immediately see that the raw materials fit our subject.

Essential oils are not in fact oils at all but are mixtures of aromatic substances giving the characteristic odour to many plants, flowers and spices.

They include the zest found in citrus peels, and are the stuff of many traditional remedies for colds and stiff muscles. They are obtained from the source materials by steam distillation, and in this process eventually pass to a container along with the condensing steam, which returns to water. Aromatic, volatile oils float upon this water, and so in medieval times they were called oils – oil floats on water. Chemically they are not oils. Science applies the name *volatile* oils and contrasts them with our subject, vegetable oils, which it terms *fixed* oils. One flies off, volatises, and the other stays put. Put a drop of each on some paper and you will see the difference.

There are many quality issues surrounding essential oils. Many that are now available in retail shops are of poor quality. Being natural products, they vary by season, growing method and process, as well as where the originating plants were grown. An analogy with wine is not out of place. The best quality, as determined by fragrance, strength, or vitality, is usually only available from specialist houses by mail order. It's worth paying for the best even if twice the price. After all you are buying an aroma! It makes no sense to buy something cheap that does not have much of a smell, when the better quality can be used at half the strength and achieve twice the fragrance – it's also true economy!

Aromatherapy arrived in this country after the Second World War, and seems to have been a well-kept secret or therapy for the cognoscenti, perhaps rich and famous, over a number of years. Several events combined to change this in the mid-1980's. A seminal book, *The Art of Aromatherapy*, had been published by Robert Tisserand. Shirley Price, a Midlands teacher, began to lead courses on the subject, and to sell a range of cure-all products to the beauty industry. The Body Shop quickly saw the potential of something new and promptly took up the idea, selling a wide range of massage oils.

I bought my very first 'essential oil' from the Body Shop. I was on a riding holiday with my wife in Shropshire and was in a state of near immobility from muscles that had not been worked for years. I found this row of little bottles that just looked useful, exciting, with exotic names. I tried them in the bath with pretty good results. Only later did I find out that at this time some of the Body Shop oils were only dilutions of essential oils at around 3% in vegetable oils such as Almond. That made for the highest priced Almond Oil I have ever bought and bears out the quality point I made above. On the plus side, as no instructions were provided, I used the whole bottle in the bath. This could have been dangerous if these had been neat essential oils. Essential oils need a little education to be safely used. To make the point, only around 7 drops are used in a bath.

One other point can be made about the early Body Shop range: it established price points for the retail UK market. As Aromatherapy began to catch on, the Body Shop set the running. Its competitors did not recognise the dilution issue and so put neat oils on the market at diluted prices. To reach these low prices, some really poor quality essential oils were put onto the market.

Perhaps the greatest single impetus to Aromatherapy came from the London School of Aromatherapy (LSA) led by Tricia Davis. Her school had a certain flair, and had the advantage of not being a front for selling oils like so many others that came after. She just gave education by local workshop and distance learning. There was a strong bias to free expression, even massage as an art form. She promoted an ethic with strong holistic principles. She founded an Aromatherapy journal and she soon had one of the largest and most influential schools running. Many of her students went on to form and mould the world of Aromatherapy and so the LSA brought Aromatherapy to the masses.

The French have a system of medicine called Aromatherapie. It's not popular but was a bit fashionable at one time. It used essential oils but in a very orthodox manner. It had little in common with the UK practice, but unfortunately much of its work was borrowed to support the efficacy of essential oils in medicine. Those wanting to make Aromatherapy more scientific, more clinical, and even more professional, headed first to French medical texts and then to textbook chemistry. This route, practically ignoring the benefits of the growing English tradition, began a running confrontation with various medical authorities. It also gave the French the opportunity to 'Harmonise' European Regulations as front-runners in the rediscovered therapy. Writing in the new century, you can begin to read in French cosmetics journals right now that the 'New' thing is Aromatherapy. Neither have the French led the way in the beauty industry by promoting the use of essential oils. Rather, their medicine aromatherapie, using essential oils administered by qualified doctors either orally or anally, has held their cosmetics industry back from using essential oils as active ingredients. No mention of massage or vegetable oils either! True Aromatherapy in the English-speaking world is different – it's about well-being, relaxation, enjoyment, health, sport, and environmental fragrancing – basic human rights and freedom of choice. It's not about mainline medicine or professional status.

Vegetable oils are an intrinsic part of the *materia medica* or repertoire of an Aromatherapist in most parts of the world. In particular, the United Kingdom has promoted the use of vegetable oils as 'carriers' for essential oils used in massage. Most books about Aromatherapy on both sides of the Atlantic and in Japan promote the idea of using a carrier in which essential oils are diluted. Massage oil therapy has become the standard accepted by most therapists practising Aromatherapy. Essential oils and vegetable oils are very compatible. Essential oils are diluted in vegetable oils very easily. Essential oils love fats, butters, oils – in fact they are, in practice, like horse and cart.

The term 'carrier' oil belittles the practical value and dynamics that lie behind the ubiquitous vegetable oils. Nutritionists have long known the true value of oils and fats, and their necessity in our diet. Those therapists working with skin care should also appreciate the different values each particular oil has in meeting a need or resolving a problem. Different vegetable oils have special caring properties of their own. Aromatherapy has pioneered their use and brought them to prominence in a number of ways.

Aromatherapy became the darling of the fashion journalist in the 1990's. As a group they claim to be a stressed-out bunch, always on the run. Hardly surprising then that they got hooked into Aromatherapy, the prime relaxation therapy. Journalists promoted Aromatherapy and caused its popularity by their own endorsements. This was highly unusual. The cosmetic houses had nothing to offer, and the perfume houses wanted nothing to do with it. Hence a new series of companies were born.

One of the first companies to hit the headlines in any big way was Origins. I helped put this company together with Tessa Harris, a marketing lady with a passion for doing things right. The company style was minimal and the shop fittings all from Nature. Lots of light, Shoji paper and western oak, marble and raw plaster. The effect was stunning and way before its time. The products were high class, used natural emulsifiers and set a new standard in creams, milks and lotions. The real novelty, though, was a range of real Aromatherapy and active perfumes, and a range of vegetable oils for massage. Education was the key, and a number of booklets were available free to the public to help teach them about the benefits of natural products.

The brand was sold to Estee Lauder and the UK shops closed. Elements of the idea can now be found in a number of cosmetic ranges. Aromatherapy had made its mark and vegetable oils had gone with it. Witness the rise of Elemis, a great brand dedicated to a professional approach to Aromatherapy. Examine their treatments, and notice the exotic vegetable oils used in treatment and found in their products alongside essential oils and other actives. They consider vegetable oils actives in themselves, not inert fillers. If a quality brand like this promotes vegetable oils, then they must have some pretty good uses.

Oils and fats do not have the glamour of essential oils. It's true they lack aroma and the excitement of headline fashion, but they are always there. Indeed, the term 'fat', like 'carrier', is very negative, very unfashionable, not exciting or interesting.

In reality nothing could be further from the truth. Oils and fats have astounding benefits and fundamental applications for anyone concerned with holistic bodywork. As already mentioned, they actually form the foundation or even the actives in many formulae and expensive treatments.

"The whole is greater than the sum of its parts" is the underlying dictum of holistic practice. Every therapist in any form of bodywork, skin care or Aromatherapy should think about this principle if they claim to be holistic in practice. It means accepting there is a realm beyond chemical analysis. It is more than a buzzword. Holism demands not only a whole-person view, but also an approach to and understanding of the nature of the material used.

24

Materials can be put together to form synergies, to do more than the literature says they can. Blending vegetable oils is an art and a craft. Achieving the
right texture and effect is not easy. Learning the chemical profiles and applications takes time and effort, but the rewards in performance and achieve-
ment are great.

# 2

# *The Origin of Fats and Oils*

There are natural animal fats and natural vegetable fats. This book is about oils and fats of vegetable origin. Leaving aside ethical questions for the moment, this does not mean that animal fats and fish oils do not have benefit – they do, but most people do not favour animal-derived material for body work. The benefits or pros and cons of animal fats and dairy products in health and well-being are to do with dietary intake, not massage work.

There are also plenty of synthesised or man-made oils, waxes, and greases and inert materials like petrolatum or mineral oils. These are commonly found as formulation ingredients in cosmetics. There are even synthetic copies of beeswax. Do we really need such things? Only if we want cheap prices and are not prepared to pay for the real stuff. Then there is the question of renewable resources and the price we individually put upon Nature.

Generally, natural or holistic therapists by preference use oils and fats derived from the vegetable kingdom. Often massage therapists, unfortunately, still use the cheapest oils around just for slippage. Cheap means little value and/or mineral oil, so check out what is being used on your body when being massaged. Do you really want a coating of fine machine oil next time you go for a massage?

Oils and fats come from nuts and seeds. Trees, flowers, fruit; everything vegetable that flowers has a seed. A nut is defined as "a dry one-seeded indehiscent fruit that usually possesses a woody wall." In common terms, we think of a kernel with a hard shell such as almond, walnut, and hazelnut. The protective coat or shell is one of Nature's ways of protecting the seed or

kernel from going off or becoming rancid. Shelled nuts may be an easier consumer choice than using nutcrackers, but not necessarily the best if nutritive
value is at stake.

Seeds come in all shapes and sizes – round ones, large, small, hard-
shelled, winged, and such like. But what are they? It is important that we
realise that a plant is made of light. In effect it materialises itself from sunshine, light. A leaf, after all, is little more than a sunshine collector. A plant
constructs itself from light energy using simple sugars to provide its motivating
power to absorb and transform its structural content. Cellulose is the most
commonly known 'sugar' that gives a plant its form and structure. It is what
makes 'wood', or the 'stuff' that keeps plants upright.

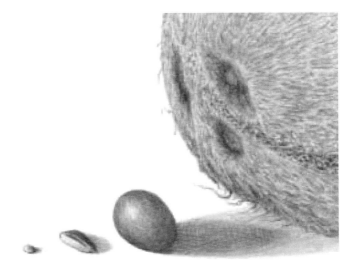

*Fig. 2.1   Various seed sizes (sesame, sunflower, olive, coconut).*

It's difficult to know what the object of a plant is. Does it have purpose?
Is it just there to feed us, look pretty, and exchange gases? Is it divine or evo-
lutionary? Undoubtedly it is alive, but in what sense? The book *The Secret
Life of Plants* explores this subject and helps us to look beyond textbook
chemistry as a model for the reality of the botanical world. It is a good read
and raises thought provoking questions about the material world around us.

We can observe and accept that the driving impulse of the plant is to flower in order to reproduce, to maintain its species existence. In essence, then, the notional power of the plant is directed toward its fertility or repro-ducibility. The pattern of the plant, its potential, is contained within the seed. Likewise the power of the plant is also contained in the seed. What do I mean by this?

The genetic code in chemical terms is nothing without the driving life force behind it to activate it. We know that a seed given ideal conditions for growth will germinate. But this is not some overt chemical action. It does mean that the conditions are right for processes to start, but the starting *is* life itself, an innate driving force or power. This energy or force has many names, but it is there, undeniable by theist or atheist alike. This drive emanates from the germ of the plant; see Fig. 2.2.

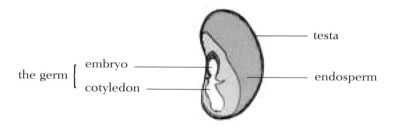

*Fig. 2.2   Inside a seed.*

When consuming bread or cereals with the germ, then, we are taking in the nutrient of the life force. Other parts of the seed play different roles. The husk or testa, for example, forms a protective layer. In cereals, when milled, we call this part the bran.

Initially seeds throw up two specialised leaves called cotyledons, and these are proto leaves. At the same time it sends out a first root or taproot. Plant a seed the wrong way up and it will try to right itself. It is programmed to seek light and moisture.

The small root quickly seeks the moist earth to begin an interchange of biological activity. Roots give out and pass into the soil sugars and weak acids to dissolve and provide minerals for itself, as well as to sustain a world of synergistic microbes and bacteria.

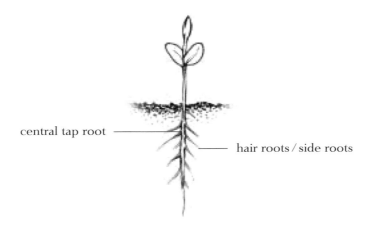

central tap root

hair roots / side roots

*Fig. 2.3 A seedling above and below ground taking in and giving out.*

If we can define a nut, what then is a seed? It is defined as a "mature fertilised plant ovule, consisting of an embryo and its food store, surrounded by a protective seed coat or testa.' This definition could well be given for a nut and, in truth, they are one and the same thing. The difference is perception rather than fact. We tend to eat nuts and to plant seeds. Beans are seeds, peas are seeds, and coconuts are seeds.

This may be a matter of interest to those with nut allergies. This is now a prominent problem as was milk allergy a few years ago. Gut allergic reactions are said to be due to an enzymatic problem or shortage. Allergies seem to follow fashions; could it be that our make-up changes? Could it be that the allergies are due to our interference with propagation or cultivation? Why should allergies to common foods that have served mankind for thousands of years suddenly appear in the last half of the $20^{th}$ century and the dawn of the $21^{st}$? Something has changed, and rapidly. Herbicides, pesticides may be the cause. Or it could be hormones or other additives built into the food chain. Maybe we should look to major pollutants. Our hunter-gatherer ancestors depended upon nuts and dried seeds to see them through the winter. They were a staple food. Such thoughts do not overcome the very real problem some experience, but should stimulate us to look further than blaming the nut! We cannot simply allow a conspiracy of government and medicine to warn us of the danger of raw foods such as nuts and blame Nature. Intelligent people should want to know what has been allowed to change Nature, including us as humans debilitating our millennia of human experience of safe foods.

External reactions to vegetable oils happen but are not common. As established, nuts and seeds are basically the same; therefore if a person reacts to one and not another, some investigation should be considered as to the origin of the problem. Could it be psychosomatic? Could it be that the oil is poor, oxidised, or contains toxins or aggressors, such as chemical residues? All matters should be considered and, as we shall see, only the best available materials used in human care.

Nuts and seeds are a storehouse for fat-soluble substances. They are likely therefore to contain pesticide or herbicide residues, assuming the biocide contained a fat-loving molecule in its structure. Nuts, too, can be a subject of radiation overdose, as at the time of the Chernobyl disaster. Low residual counts do not impress me. People can be sensitised to quite tiny amounts of a substance. Safe values for agricultural chemicals are measured for each individual chemical. We should be concerned about what we may call the cocktail effect. Seeds, and nuts too, are centres of concentration, energy storage depots for the future potential plant. Any fat soluble chemical will be stored in the seed or nut.

## What Makes Growth?

A seed or nut contains the germ of life, the pattern of existence and inherent purpose, the DNA. The genome project has taught us that the possible variations and diversity of Nature allows for more than DNA, an extra something yet to be found. Once conditions are right, growth is inevitable. Life itself is a driving force as yet incomprehensible to materialistic science. To power this growth, nuts and seeds must have full or stored energy.

Life force is not necessarily power, and each viable seed contains within itself a storehouse of fuel. This fuel is needed to power the plant in its first few hours whilst developing itself as a light-activated organism running on starch and sugars. The stored fuel it consumes also originated from the sun. *It is the vegetable fats and oils that are the stored fuels.* This basic energy dump maintains plant growth after its initial life force kick-starts the new plant. The quality and size of the store in part determines the viability of the plant. Vegetable oils and fats have, then, valuable dynamics and properties in themselves. Liz Earle in her book called them 'Vital Oils'. I wholeheartedly agree with the sentiment expressed in her title.

As has been said, a leaf is a sunshine collector; a collector of sun energy to activate photosynthesis whereby light energy is taken to plant cells and stored as they separate the oxygen from water. Until the first leaves are formed, a plant must rely upon its stored energy – its fat store within the seed or nut – for its impetus and fuel. Fat, of course, is a more concentrated energy store than, say, sugar. In terms of diet, we think of calories or the amount of heat energy available. Most slimmers are quite aware of this energy measure. In sunflower seeds or grains, 300-330 calories is about right for 100 grams. A potato weighing 100 grams, on the other hand, containing starch or, put another way, slow sugar, has only 90 calories. The energy potential of seeds and nuts is then very impressive.

Can we say more? In practice many therapists have found vegetable oils to be more effective than they had anticipated. Some favour the view that this is the result of an interchange between therapist and client or patient. Others hypothesize that any result may simply be the placebo effect. This whole seed 'idea' reminds me of the controversy that exists concerning homoeopathy and such ideas of the memory of water. Such a memory is implicit within the seed. The potential or purpose of the plant is right there – fact. The plant will, in effect, come into being, yielding itself into a preformed electrical field. Plants are not only physical and material things, but, like us, have 'electrical' properties and energy potentials. Surely the biomass of the seed, if processed perfectly, could yield more than we expect, perhaps the whole potential of the purpose of the plant. This seems to match experience. A fanciful idea? Yes, but one born of practical experience. Plants are born by soil, but are the product of pure sunshine.

## The Value of Fats and Oils

For an Aromatherapist, there has to be an understanding of the relationship between essential oils and their 'carriers.' The essential oil is soluble in the 'carrier' oil but there is also a more symbiotic relationship, which, although appreciated by practitioners in the UK, is hardly explored. Commercially biased exponents and writers in and on this new, popular therapy concentrated mainly on essential oils -the area where they could make the quickest gain and most profit. The carrier oil as an active substance was largely ignored.

Vegetable oils can, in fact, often be used in practice without the necessity for essential oils. Vegetable oils are part of the basic working tools of an Aromatherapist, and should be more appreciated and used by all concerned.

If the English-speaking world has indeed produced a new 'tradition' in Aromatherapy, then it owes a lot to the medicine or health and beauty treatments of the East, and even Africa. Oil massage has been valued for its benefits for thousands of years. Touch alone has significant benefit, as has soft tissue manipulation and bone setting. There are specialist activities such as lymph drainage massage. Then, of course, which mother does not stroke, hold or massage her baby. Massage is essential to most effective forms of Aromatherapy. Effective massage usually requires a lubricant to reduce friction and supply slippage. Never divorce the two ideas, massage from its lubricant. One should, therefore, use a lubricant that also does something good for the receiver. This is basic to folk tradition.

An example of folk use can be found in Africa where, on the West Coast, a butter from the fruit of the Shea tree is a pretty universal panacea. Shea butter has been a staple of traditional medicine here for as long as anyone can remember. It's said that Cleopatra imported the butter for her cosmetic use! Mungo Park, the Scots explorer, was the first European to record

*Ancient olive tree on Crete*

*Olive branch with fruits*

*Olive groves in France*

*Walnut trees near Poitiers, France*

*The author examining walnut trees*

*Apricot trees in winter, Les Beaux de Provence, France*

*Sunflowers, near St. Pantaleon, France*

*Milk Thistle, near Chartres, the herb garden of France*

*Field of St. Johns Wort, Loire Valley, France*

its virtues. However the cultures of North Africa were writing about it in the 14th century.

In the 1940's it was noted that in places where the population used Shea butter as an emollient and protector, the occurrence of skin disease was far less common than in other areas. Various skin disorders are part of everyday life in some tropical countries. The chemistry of Shea butter does not seem to add up to much. Shea butter either has hidden properties or it improves the skins resistance to disease. Either way, it does a good job. Everyone knows the use of Shea butter makes for a supple and smooth skin, and it can be found as a base in the best creams around. It is also used as a traditional remedy for alleviating rheumatism, indicating anti-inflammatory properties, again taking it a step further than its obvious contents. Processing of the raw butter can lead to positive or negative effects. Not all oils and butters are what they seem, and can be a far cry from the traditional or natural material.

Unsurprisingly, Shea butter or Karité is a foundation substance in the better quality professional Aromatherapy base materials too, whether cream or balm bases. Practicing, better qualified Aromatherapists have long valued the activity of such noble materials, realising too that bases rich in such oils give a very efficient release of the actives incorporated into the massage cream or unguent. Some results show this can be up to 24% better than BP ointment or paraffin based material

As with most things, the quality of the starting or raw materials play a significant part in the potential activity of the product. Ecologically correct products, those from traditional sources, from mechanical pressing and considered 'natural' in consumer terms, lie alongside industrially produced material from solvent (hexane) extraction processes. The performance varies. The price sometimes tells the difference.

Unfortunately, many Aromatherapy schools just gloss over this important subject of vegetable oils. This is partly due to a shortage of information, but I believe also partly due to commercial reasons. Many schools and tutors sell essential oils. This trade, by its nature, seems, on the surface, to be simple. It is not, as many have found to their cost. The trade in Fats and

Oils is more complex. It requires large volume stock holding and proper storage under Nitrogen, as at Fragrant Earth. This problem of storage, volume and access keeps people out of the business. Recently I was handed a bottle of Organic Almond Oil from a supplier well known for their bargain prices. Alas, as the student has surmised, it was rancid, unpleasant to smell and a real waste of money. Organic or any other quality label does not always mean best. The buyer has to be objective and realistic.

Cooking oil is often equated with edible oil, and quality values are not assessed properly – the student is sometimes pushed to supermarket shelves, rather than being taught the difference in values of starting material and oil processing. These affect end quality and results. *Quality should be defined as fit for a purpose.* So the quality may differ for the same variety or species depending upon the end purpose. Define the purpose and then decide the quality. Lamp oil or refined cooking oil has its place, as does massage oil. The two or three may cross function to some degree but they do have different values, processes and results.

There are a large number of vegetable oils, all of which have important characteristics in their own right. A number of them can be used internally for nutritional purposes, as well as externally. A true Aromatherapist should become as familiar with the quality of their vegetable oils as with their essential oils. If giving dietary advice it should be remembered that not all oils are of Food grade. Make certain you are sure of the quality that is used.

If you feel there is some doubt about all this, let us look at the historical way essential oils were used and extracted. I have no hard evidence, but on balance I favour the idea that distillation was invented in pre-historic times, and that the method was lost at some point. What is certain is that by the time of Hippocrates, say about 450 BC, the use of aromatic health and beauty care, which is what we are really talking about when we use the term 'aromatherapy,' was in common use. It is probably true that his Greek medicine itself was drawn from prior Assyrian and perhaps even Indian or Chinese documents acquired at the time of Alexander the Great.

By the time of Dioscorides, around 60 CE, a well-documented system of herbal/aromatic treatments and therapies existed. Roman medicine was basically reassessed Greek medicine. Galen, physician to Roman Emperors, was the most famous of their physicians. We think of these treatments as having traditional Western medicine roots, but the Roman Empire was not entirely Western, it extended eastward. We tend to forget that for a good part, Constantinople, Byzantium, in the latter Empire days was heavily influenced by Central Asia; eventually falling under Islamic rule, it is at this point that we begin to witness the recorded use of distillation.

Generally speaking, most attribute distillation techniques to Avicenna, often and erroneously called an Arab. He is in fact claimed as a Tajik coming from Central Asia, and is associated with the great learning centres and cities of Bokhara and Samarkand.

Let's turn our attention back to the herbal treatments of Galen, which were both effective and often aromatic. They were not tinctures as we think of them today, and as used by most modern herbalists. They surely would have included aromatic wines and vinegars taken as drink and used as frictions. There must have been decoctions, brews, and water extracts, but the Romans are known not to have been very hot on herbal teas!

## Infused or Herbal Oils

To examine and understand the extraction methods used for plants, and what really happened, it is best to look at traditional societies that have survived to our own day. In such societies we find that the commonest solvent or medicine when a fresh herb is not available is a maceration or fat extraction, making herbal oils. It is common to see in Africa, for example, goat fat used as an extract solvent. A herb is macerated in the fat and then smeared on the body. I have seen many of these preparations supplied by local medicine men, or sangomas. Some certainly do not smell so good, but in discussion these 'aromatherapy unguents' are said to be popular and effective. People from Slavic or even Scandinavian countries will be familiar with the history of smearing bears' grease or goose grease, which would have contained herbs, on to the body. In Saxon times even butter would have been used as a herb solvent, and even today, you may be familiar with herbal butters such as the common garlic butter. In warmer climates, of course, animal fats were not needed. The solvent would have been much better, in other words, vegetable oil – princi-pally Olive Oil.

Notice how we have come full circle. True, traditional or classical Aro-matherapy has always encompassed the use of aromatic materials extracted from the plant via a vegetable oil or fatty substance. This is a true or classical Aromatherapy as much as the use of essential oils extracted by steam. Essen-tial oils should not be divorced from their cousins the vegetable oils.

Think of the traditional process for a moment. A substance, such as Olive Oil, has added to it a wound-healing herb, such as Hypericum perfora-tum, St. John's Wort. It is allowed to steep and stand in the sun, macerated over a period of weeks. Eventually, a rich, ruby red, spicy smelling oil is drawn off, followed by simple filtration. The residue is returned to the compost heap and back into the natural cycle. The plant has yielded through the maceration not only its essential oil component, but other fat-soluble parts too. Notice, please, the essential oil is very difficult to extract from Hypericum perforatum by distillation; it does not yield well. The essential oil is very, very expensive – costing hundreds of pounds per kilo. The maceration, on the other hand, is an easy process and provides relatively cheap, ready-to-use, effective thera-peutic oil.

Today, we call these **herbal oils, infused oils, or phytols.** *Phyto* meaning plant and *ol* short for oleum or oil. (Phytol also refers to a specific group of chemicals, so be clear in your context if using the term.)

These herbal oils, or infused oils, are most likely what Galen and his predecessors would have considered their main medicinal resource. Think, too, of the earlier Egyptian papyri, which contain references to salves, oint-ments and unguents – all a form of fat or oil extraction. These extraction methods are still common in Africa today.

With this in mind, let's go back to our St. John's Wort extract (H. per-foratum). What is the value or advantage of this traditional method even over distillation? Well, there are several. Due to the nature of the solvent, not only is essential oil extracted but also a variety of other fat-soluble substances. For example, fat-soluble vitamins, waxes and other potent chemicals are absorbed in minute amounts.

The logic of what has been said so far is clear, and I am sure that you can see the advantage of using these extracts in practice and in the home or salon. Why add expensive essential oil to vegetable oil when often you can get the same or more benefit from this traditional method? It is not the amount of essential present that matters but the effect. There are other reasons for following the route of adding essential oils to 'carriers' and much to do with aroma values, but at least the alternative herbal oils should be given more consideration. I am sure you will see far more of them in cosmetics and medicine in the next few years.

# 3

# *What is Oil?*

$L$et us now return to the central point. Does the vegetable oil or fat contribute anything within itself to a treatment? The answer is complex and requires a reasonable understanding of process technology. You may have understood so far what fat is, what it looks like – but what, really, is an oil? You can see fat in nuts but not oil, or can you?

From a chemical point of view, there is no difference between a fat and oil. It is really just to do with temperature. For example, coconut butter or fat is solid in the average north European room temperature, except in the summer when it turns from being a fairly solid lump to a runny substance.

There is no need to get too complicated about the chemistry of fats, but we should understand the very basics. This is not meant to be a chemistry textbook so the following should be used simply as an aid to understanding why oil is beneficial and needed for life. A good chemistry textbook about fats should be sought if fuller information is required.

Vegetable oils are organic compounds containing carbon, hydrogen and oxygen. Oils and fats differ from one another mainly in the amount and variety of fatty acids they contain. Fatty acids are long hydro carbon chains attached to what is termed carboxyl group (more of this later). The group of fats that we are interested in are called **triglycerides**, the more modern name is triacylglycerols but is still not so commonly used.

The term 'lipid' is applied to fats and oils. It could be termed the posh name, the scientific name, and in popular literature is generally interchangeable. Whilst all fats are indeed lipids, not all lipids are true fats. There are many substances associated with or found in fats that have the characteristic of not mixing or dissolving in water. This latter characteristic is a simple and not always accurate way of deciding whether something is an oil or not.

The content of Fatty Acids may distinguish one oil or fat from another but they alone do not make up a fat. An essential, and the main, component of a fat molecule is **glycerol** (the common name is glycerine), a special sort of alcohol. It is a trihydric alcohol. Its structure and its derivation are related to **carbohydrates.** The fatty acids to which it is attached have a different base route. Alcohols and acids can combine together to form **esters,** and this is what happens when combinations of glycerol and fatty acids form fats. Fats and oils are compounds of three fatty acids, the same or different, linked to one molecule of glycerol – different combinations of triglycerides. Some fatty acids are called 'essential', meaning that the body cannot synthesise them but we have to ingest them to be healthy. Linoleic acid and linolenic acid are the two essential fatty acids.

Every carbon atom can form four chemical bonds. A carbon atom can be likened to a four-legged octopus. It can link and grab other atoms or fold back on itself. This ability or covalence enables long chains or branches to form. Fatty Acids are molecules with a particular arrangement of atoms at the end of each chain. This ending is of one carbon atom, two of oxygen and one of hydrogen (-COOH) thus forming what is called the carboxyl group. It can be written out as in Fig. 3.1., which illustrates Oleic acid.

```
      H H H H H H H H H  H H H H H H H H H
      |  |  |  |  |  |  |  |  |   |  |  |  |  |  |  |  |  |
  H - C - C - C - C - C - C - C - C - C = C - C - C - C - C - C - C - C - C - COOH
      |  |  |  |  |  |  |  |                  |  |  |  |  |  |  |
      H H H H H H H H               H H H H H H H
```

*Fig. 3.1.   Oleic acid chain with 18 carbons*

The quality or the use of the oil will very often depend upon the fatty acid profile or the fatty acids it contains. These fairly large oil molecules often have, especially when referring to nutrition, the terms 'saturated' or 'unsaturated' applied to them. Most people will be familiar with the terms and probably have taken on board the idea from TV advertisements that 'saturated = bad' and 'unsaturated = good'. This over simplification is not at all helpful.

The very name 'fatty acid' comes from the fact that they were first found in animal fats, which are generally solid, dense. Saturated fats are mainly of animal origin, from meat and dairy products, but there are also vegetable saturated fats such as coconut and palm also solid, dense. Saturated fats are quite resistant to oxidation and so can be stored more easily and longer, they are stable at normal northern room temperatures. Older people will recognise this as a characteristic of Lard. Saturated fats are usually high in cholesterol, and due to this, have been put into a negative light relative to heart disease. The facts do not equate with this overly simplistic view.

In simple terms, because we do not want to be confused by the chemistry, a saturated fat contains the maximum number of hydrogen atoms possible in its chain. The chain is full or saturated. An unsaturated fat lacks a certain number of hydrogen atoms: it has an open chain where other atoms can be attached, and can be filled further. This is like a chain with some weaknesses. We call these areas 'a discontinuity', or the more familiar chemistry term, 'a double bond'. The carbon atom reaches back to itself rather than attaching to a hydrogen atom. A double bond is therefore like a weakness; it becomes a possible centre of reaction for oxygen. In other words, it's prone to oxidation or rancidity. On the good side, the chain can be broken down more easily by digestion.

Double bonds also introduce the idea of form, structure or shape to a molecule. Mostly we see molecular formulae written out in linear form, as for example Oleic fatty acid, which we could write as $C_{17}H_{33}COOH$. A sort of shorthand is used in chemistry to tell us the number of atoms present in a molecule. The example of oleic acid shows 17 carbon atoms present, plus 33 hydrogen atoms along with the carboxyl group. The chain is formed or based on carbon, so we could simply call this C18 and leave it at that. So for myristic fatty acid read C14, or for palmitic fatty acid read C16.

In reality the molecule will have a very real shape; it does not actually look like writing but exists in a real form or shape. In our digestion, enzymes look for certain shapes; they 'fit' certain shapes. The more double bonds the molecule chain has, the more flexible or easily broken down it becomes; we can even say the more 'oily' or loose the material is, especially if the chain is a long one. The chain lengths we are mostly interested in are between 10 to 24 carbons long.

It follows that if fats and oils are chains of carbon, hydrogen, and oxygen, then logically the difference between one and another is simply the length of the chain. To a certain extent this holds true but it is not the whole story. Nature is deceptively simple. Lauric acid is a 12-carbon chain, myristic acid 14, palmitic acid 16, and stearic acid 18 – all nicely different. However, look above and notice the number of carbons in oleic acid- it too has 18 carbons. So what makes the difference? How can something appear to be the same and yet be different?

The problem often lies in a poor perception of so-called science. Like the proverbial doctor's handwriting, which intentionally obscures much, in old times and certainly until recent years, science has been written only for the informed. This entrenched view was based upon the need to be *exclusive*, that one had to learn the language to be qualified to earn esteem or even a salary. The common person was excluded! True science is really observation, record, and informed guesswork, and open to all. $H_2O$ actually sounds more impressive than water but it is only a shorthand for water. What really counts is the observation of the water, what form it is in, what it does. Is it ice, steam, liquid? Such things are the same, have the same formula but perform differently. Circumstances such as temperature produce change without changing the obvious makeup. So straight-line formulae are sometimes confusing because we are simply put off by the figures or the code. They do not tell the whole story, as we have seen in the example of water. Likewise with fats and oils. Formulae are useful, and are of course a help, if we can understand the code.

Let's look at this word 'bond' again. We could misunderstand the nature of chemical bonding by thinking that when fatty acids are put with glycerol they are just mixed up, stirred in, so to speak, like sugar in tea. This idea is quite wrong. Bonds are for life. They make definite chemical changes to form something new; they are not mixtures. They are reactive, the components bonded into a combination with potentials beyond the uncombined parts.

If double bonds are weaknesses then something without them is stronger, less prone to go off. We have mentioned the ability of oxygen to react to or break down at these bonds, but of course bonds can also be broken down or metabolised through our digestion. If just one double bond exits in a chain, then the fatty acid is termed *monounsaturated*. If more than one double bond exists, then it is termed *polyunsaturated*. Oleic acid is monounsaturated whilst Arachidonic acid has four double bonds. The obvious difference then between stearic acid and oleic acid is the bonding. Bonds make differences. So stearic acid is C18, and oleic acid, with its one double bond, we write as C18:1. Linoleic acid also has 18 carbons but two double bonds, written as C18:2, and linolenic acid has three double bonds and so becomes C18:3. Arachidonic acid has twenty carbons and four double bonds so we have C20:4, a polyunsaturated oil.

Hydrocarbon chains can bend at their double bonds. This means the chain will twist; irregular shapes and angles from a straight chain will occur. Saturated fats would stack up like bricks, whereas unsaturated fats could be described as crumpled up or like a torn, Xmas paper chain. So apart from temperature, saturation too plays a role in what we could call natural tendencies toward solidity or mobility.

No doubt most of us have seen the word 'hydrogenation' on margarine packs. We can now begin to see that adding hydrogen atoms to a liquid polyunsaturated fat will harden it. This is the basis for the manufacture of margarine. Popular today are spreads that are partially hydrogenated with the intent of maintaining a supply of polyunsaturated fatty acids. Polyunsaturated fats, it is said, tend to lower blood cholesterol. Hardening polyunsaturates changes nature. Double bonds are destroyed or their nature transformed. From the manufacturers point of view, shelf life is improved and where only partial hydrogenation takes place, an easy-to-spread product is contrived but without the nature or the content of the original oil that may itself have been rich in unsaturated fatty acids.

Oils from a particular plant species, seed or nut, maintain a variety of fatty acids of different types. It would be easy at this stage to confuse each separate fatty acid with a specific oil; however, they are not one and the same thing. Where the fatty acids with only one double bond predominate, the *oil itself* is described as monounsaturated. Such is the case for olive, sweet almond, and macadamia. With a certain amount of natural resistance to oxidation, they make good general-purpose oils. Polyunsaturated oils including passionflower, corn, and evening primrose, all of which have more than one double bond, are more readily damaged by heat, light exposure to air, and even moisture. The carboxyl group, at the end of the chain, has an affinity to water, which can present some problems for storage.

In practical terms, in Aromatherapy the polyunsaturated oils are blended both with saturated or monounsaturated oils to form blends for beneficial massage. They can also form the active ingredients in creams, milks, and gels. The more polyunsaturated oils are used, the greater the need for original oil freshness, good storage facilities by your supplier, and to consider issues of preservation if making products with 'shelf life'.

There is another issue concerning double bonds that becomes very important in determining what personal philosophies we may have regarding natural matters. Keeping all that you have just read to one side, let us return to where a vegetable oil comes from, its source. Not only do we have to determine what it is and what it is composed of, but also what it represents.

Reminding ourselves that all these vegetable oils come from Nature can now be very important to some of us, because Nature is a delicate and balanced substance, an 'idea' even. We are a part of that natural process and we are what we eat. We can only process into our own metabolism that which is taken in, absorbed, not eliminated. The quality of our food and our ability to process it eventually reflects the quality of our body or our health, our well-being, ourselves. We synthesise ourselves from foods.

We need now to refer to this very important diagram and concept shown in Fig. 3.2.

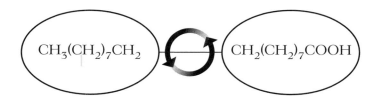

*Fig. 3.2   STEARIC ACID saturated, 18 carbons with a point of rotation.*

Here we see illustrated stearic acid written as a straight line, and we can see that two portions of the molecule can rotate for example around an axis between C9 and C10. C with a number after it is simply shorthand for how many carbons there are before the –COOH carboxyl group. With oleic acid we can see that because of the double bond, there cannot be any rotation between the two carbons. This allows for the fact that there will be a structure that is very close to oleic acid but not identical to it in shape. What this shows is that when two structures are written out in a straight line, they can be very different when their configuration and shape are taken into account. If the double bond could rotate or was a single bond, they would be the same thing.

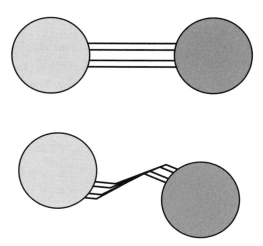

*Fig. 3.3   A double bond can distort not rotate.*

In other words, something can have the same linear formula but have a different geometry. This is termed **cis/trans isomerism.** The *cis* form is the natural form with the Hydrogen atoms on the same side. The *trans* or synthetic form has opposing atoms.

To help identify oils in a simple way, the numbering system referred to above can be extended. So the fatty acid is not only identified by the number of carbon atoms in the chain, for example palmitoleic acid C16, but also by the number of double bonds it has, therefore C16:1. Linoleic acid, as we have noted with two double bonds, would be identified as C18:2. Sometimes even the position of the double bonds are given, so for the important Linoleic acid it could be written as C18:2, 9c 12c. Here the c refers to the cis form, and the last two numbers to the position in the carbon chain of the double bond.

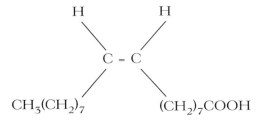

OLEIC ACID
18 carbons. Cis form, both hydrogens on the same side.

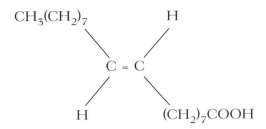

ELAIDIC ACID
18 carbons. Trans form.
The same linear formula but different in configuration.

*Fig. 3.4   Same constituents but different shapes.*

These different forms, cis and trans, may look the same in one way but they are not the same. In my lectures I ask students if their hands are identical. This generates some discussion but we normally come to the conclusion that they are, bar a few wrinkles. Next I ask the student to try on or imagine putting a left-hand glove on the right hand. They soon get the point that hands, like mirror images, are diametrically opposite in aspect and in performance. This illustration fits the different isomers well. One fits nature; the other is questionable. Natural isomers are easily assimilated. The synthetic, not so. Trans oils, whatever their theoretical makeup, may well behave like saturated fats doing little for blood cholesterol levels perhaps even becoming centres of irritation.

Fats are broken down into their useful parts in the body by enzymes. Enzymes are like catalysts; they fit only one particular action. They too have shape and form. To work properly they need to fit exactly into the situation or activity. A rough fit may not work, or even cause an irritation. The special enzymes connected with fat metabolism, lipases, are no different. Hence many doubt the nutritive value of trans form fats in the diet – too many definitely cause problems. It's not unreasonable to conclude that they are at the bottom of some allergic reactions. If a biofeedback objection has been built to a particular trans fatty acid, it is not unreasonable to suggest that allergic reactions could result either from ingestion or even topical application.

By moving one hydrogen atom to the other side of the chain, the two, in effect, now balance each other, ironing out any kinks in the chain, and changing the shape. The kinks in the cis form allow vital chemical reactions to take place. Trans fatty acids are similar enough to the normal to allow them to be built into cell membranes. This could possibly create havoc with cellular activity, from the production of energy to anti-inflammatory actions or prostaglandin production. Remember we are what we eat.

Returning to the points made earlier about unsaturated fatty acids, oxidation and rancidity, high temperatures will also change the nature of fat from a *cis* form to a *trans* form, from a natural to an unnatural. This becomes very important as to whether your body can use the material made available to it internally or externally. This factor applies to processing or pressing the raw material to obtain the oil as much as it does to cooking.

Therapists should logically be asking themselves questions as to what they are really recommending to their patients or clients. It is not a question of brand name or advertising hype, but rather the effect the oil is meant to achieve. In the end it does not matter whether the oil is for use internally or externally. What matters is the bioavailability of the material.

Surely a client or patient seeking expert advice can expect something better than what is readily available in stores. It is not then simply a matter of what is the cheapest oil available to a salon or clinic, or what deal can be struck by the NHS buyer or hospital pharmacy, but rather what is the best material available to suit the purpose specified. Consumers should follow the same principles. Leave the cooking oil for the purpose intended, perhaps even questioning its value for that purpose. A good question concerning all naturals, a guiding rule of thumb, is to avoid things that do not go off. Ask why do they have immortality? If bacteria cannot feed on something or oxygen cannot break it down easily, then neither can we.

## Minor Components

One group of very important and active substances found in natural oils are *phospholipids or phosphatides*. We can think of the granular powder that may be added to your breakfast cereal. It's called Lecithin. Lecithin as a dietary supplement is viewed as a sort of cholesterol-buster. The main work that lecithins do is emulsification, joining water and oil and thereby aiding the body to absorb and breakdown fats and oils. Plentiful circulating lecithin stops the artery walls becoming 'sticky', so allowing cholesterol to circulate freely. Some oils are naturally richer than others in lecithin.

Phospholipids are particularly important for the special fatty myelin covering, or sheath, common to nerve cells and the brain. Chemically, as the group name implies, they are fatty substances with phosphorous at their heart. They are very active materials but still with the usual fat components of carbon, oxygen and hydrogen.

As cooks will know, egg yolk is an emulsifier. It is part of every mayonnaise. The reason for this is its lecithin content which is around 6% or more. High-class cosmetics also use this oily egg yolk extract as an emulsifier, either on its own or in combination as a co-emulsifier. The name 'lecithin' is derived from the Greek word *likithos*, meaning egg yolk. Lecithin, like soap, has ends to its molecule that either love or hate water. It forms the base of high-class and expensive non-soap shampoos and cleansers.

An emulsifier is something that has the dual property of both loving and hating water. It can therefore combine the two, as in a cosmetic. Emulsifiers are part of a group of what are called 'surface active chemicals'. Surprisingly, we all say 'oil and water do not mix.' Yet it is from oils that we derive a number of natural detergents. Lecithin is an emollient, antioxidant and thickener. It's a vital substance for natural therapists!

Skin care products using lecithins in their formulation have remarkable touch and caring properties. Due to its emulsifying properties, skin cleansers made with lecithin, either from oily egg yolk extract or other vegetable sources such as Soya beans, give very soft and effective cleansing actions. They are especially beneficial for sensitive and oily skins.

These days one should also be sure, if using vegetable lecithins from Soya beans, that they do not come from Genetically Modified Organisms. Soya imported from the US has invariably been contaminated this way, as have many cereal crops.

Whilst dietary considerations are always written about lecithin due to its anti cholesterol activity, there are other important health benefits. Products rich in phospholipids are very useful for skin health in such conditions as psoriasis and eczema.

Cholesterol reduction in the bloodstream is in part due to the solubising or emulsifying characteristics of lecithins. The deposition of cholesterol on artery walls is unlikely if high levels of emulsifiers are present. Vitamin activity too is probably enhanced. Carotene, the precursor to vitamin A, is more readily absorbed and utilised. Inositol and choline (B vitamin complex components), needed in fat metabolism, are certainly present in the phospholipids.

Another important group of components found in oils and fats are called 'sterols' (Phytosterols) – not to be confused with prescription or body building steroids! Sterols are essential cell components with structural functions, but are also hormone precursors. Phytosterols, plant sterols, are common minor substances, structurally close to cholesterol. Some are common; some are rare with big effects. The D-7 series, stigmasterols (schottenol and spinasterol), are not common and oils containing these should be noted. Work in Mexico suggests these are anti-cancer agents.

Cell membrane stability and skin moisturisation have both been demonstrated to have improved with topical applications of plant sterols, as has wound healing, burns, and leprosy. Anti-inflammatory action has been noted on the skin. If you want to use the benefits of Phytosterols, then aim for the most natural sources. Aromatherapists will spot immediately the value of such components and probably begin to realise that properties given to essential oils (e.g. plant hormones) more correctly lie with the so- called carrier oils or herbal oils. Cold pressed crude oils for topical applications, alongside dietary intake of whole grain cereals, brown rice, and unbleached flours, are most useful sources.

Cholesterol probably deserves a place of its own if only because it has received bad press coverage. In the public mind it is the cause of coronary heart disease (CHD). This is not always true. First it is essential to the body, and in particular cell membranes where most of it is found. It is the starting material in the synthesis for many vital chemical messengers such as hormones. The liver manufactures cholesterol as well as it being taken in through diet. It is only a problem when it is deposited on artery walls, so making them 'furry' or prone to blockage by clots, or when it crops up as gallstones. The reason why it deposits is the problem, not the substance itself. Of course there may be a correlation between quantity and deposition but the cause of deposition should be a main concern.

Cholesterol is circulated attached to proteins, lipoproteins, of which there are two types. Commonly you read that there are two types of cholesterol rather than reference to lipoprotein types. The first type is LDL (low density lipoprotein) and the second is HDL (high density lipoprotein). Blood plasma, being a watery substance, cannot transport fat in solution. The body's answer is to combine a lipid with a protein. Lipoproteins include the phospholipids and even the macrophages or white blood cells. Anyway, the point is that LDL, which is nearly pure cholesterol, takes some time to break down and can accumulate in the blood. HDL, on the other hand, breaks down quickly and even seems to protect against heart disease. If there is a cause for deposition of cholesterol, then LDL is not what you want circulating. Over refinement of fats and oils would be bad news if you were ingesting oil because the trans fatty acid from refined oils is said to actually increase LDL cholesterol and lower the HDL cholesterol! Phytosterols present in an oil can reduce the 'bad' LDL without reducing the 'good' HDL.

Not to be overlooked are the Phytoestrogens, isoflavones, which again are hormone-like substances, steroids, which can reduce the level of free oestrogen in the body so lowering the risk of oestrogen responsive cancers such as breast cancer. Many oilseeds and cereals contain such substances or at least their precursors. The Avellana species have special properties in this direction.

Fat-soluble vitamins are A, D, E and K. In low fat diets, deficiencies will occur. Fat, though, as we have seen, is a storage system, so too much of a good thing can occur with these vitamin types. Vitamin A comes in two types. Retinol is the functional form, or pre-formed type found in animal fats only; the carotenoids or carotenes are the type found in vegetable oils, and are precursors of vitamin A. Whilst retinol is stored in the liver, carotenes are not. So with vegetable sources, requiring a conversion process, toxicity due to overdose is not an issue.

In the third world, poor dietary intake of fats leading to poor eyesight and night blindness is well known. Those countries also suffer from poor skin and mucosa conditions, which are also a sign of vitamin A deficiency.

Carotenes belong to the large family of carotenoids numbering about five hundred in all. They are natural colouring pigments, from yellow through orange to red, and give the colour to such things as oranges, swedes, and carrots.

Carotenes also function as antioxidants whilst retinol does not. Some evidence suggests they reduce cancer risks. They are free radical scavengers in their own right, and so anti-agers. Increasingly their value is recognised not in a cosmetic sense but in terms of whole body health. After all, most disease is as a result of ageing or the loss of body defence mechanisms that just wear out.

Normally we would immediately think of tocopherol for this function as an antioxidant, commonly known as vitamin E. This vitamin comes from the germ of the plant; it supports life. Vitamin E has an important role not only as a highly effective antioxidant for the protection of polyunsaturated fatty acids, but other cell membrane components too. It also functions as an anti-inflammatory and immune system stimulant.

Strictly speaking, we should say 'Tocopherols'. Oils may contain alpha, beta, gamma and delta types or isomers. Alpha tocopherol is the most active. The term 'vitamin E' covers another substance, tocotrienol, which along with alpha tocopherol protects cell membranes from damage by free radicals. Low-density lipoprotein (LDL) is also protected by vitamin E from oxidation. Tocopherols, next to carotenes, are the most important antioxidants in the human cell.

Vitamin D comes as two types, 2 and 3 (strangely there is no 1). It is normally obtained only from animal sources such as milk, but its absorption is dependent upon the phytate content of plants. Vitamin D is often described as the sunshine vitamin as it is formed in the skin when the skin is exposed to light. It is thought that it may be better described as a hormone rather than a vitamin. D3 is the natural type whilst D2 (ergocalciferol) is synthetic and is the type usually found as a supplement.

Vitamin D has functions in relation to calcium maintenance and bone structure. New evidence suggests that it does far more, being implicated now in cell proliferation or abundance and cell life or maturation. The sole vegetable source is reputed to be Avocado Oil.

Phylloquinone, menaquinone and menadione are probably not known outside the expert field. They represent vitamin K and it is needed to form the blood clotting agent, prothrombin. The first name comes from green vegetable and seed oil sources, but gut bacteria are perhaps the key source and are responsible for the second named substance. The last named type is the synthetic variant. It does not take much thought to see this is not a substance to overdose on! Warfarin, a well-known rat poison, is used as a medication to reduce coagulation. Clearly the two do not go together.

Understanding even a little of the chemistry of fats and oils enables us to see what a valuable substance these treasures are. Unsung and not highly regarded, they do a great deal for our health and well-being. We find them in the most unexpected places – in the kitchen, on the dressing table, in the bathroom, even in the workshop.

# 4

# *Making An Oil*

The processing of the source material, the nuts and seeds, will have an effect upon the benefit that can be derived from the resulting oils, butters, and fats. In practical reality, the process is probably more important than the original raw materials. After all, there is little point in paying a premium for an Organic oil if it has been overheated to death, or paying for a crude oil that goes rancid the moment it is open. A really balanced and unemotional view is needed to make intelligent choices for a specific application. Not all refining is bad, not all that is crude is harmless or good.

Let us begin to look at some of the processes that oils may go through before reaching us as users, consumers or therapists. In these pages we can only generalise. Each plant or factory, called 'a mill', will have different or special techniques. Oil mills differ widely, there are trade secrets. Oil is a mass market, and we should dispel the idea of village communities or families pounding away at oil seeds to meet major consumer demands. Undoubtedly some specialist suppliers may have such material from time to time. Some traveller may bring back a speciality, but they are not available for general use. Oils originate in mills and refineries, large and small. Some are sympathetic to natural or holistic markets; others are not.

Oils come from seeds, big seeds or little seeds. Some seeds are well known as oil bearing, such as Sweet Almond, Palm or Linseed. Linseed Oil first came to my attention as a boy when oiling my cricket bat. It was the preferred substance. The story of Linseed Oil and how it is processed shows the extent to which industrialisation can be applied to an oil.

Linseed comes from the flax plant and is grown all over the world. It can be recognised when in flower by fields of soft blue brightening up the countryside. It is an ancient plant whose fibres give us the fabric we call linen. The oil is sold in health food shops as Flax Seed Oil. It makes a good cattle 'cake' or winter food. The hot pressed oil has long been used extensively in the arts as the pigment solvent in oil painting, as well as in varnishes and general domestic paint. Soft soap often had a Linseed base. The oil has a strange feeling of dryness and, when oxidised, becomes a semi flexible solid. Old-fashioned oilcloth and Linoleum (Lin from Linseed and oleum the Latin for oil) are products of this feature. When sulphur is added, a vulcanised rubber substitute is formed. All that this tells us is that Linseed Oil is generally going to be highly processed!

In principle I suppose all seeds can be made to yield an oil but, as with essential oils, some are difficult to persuade to give up their bounty. The process that they may have to go through can be not only long and complicated, but also destructive to nutrients and, at the same time, produce bi-products that are toxic. For instance, the trans fatty acids formed in the heating process should be viewed as undesirable toxins.

The basic process can be simple and was, and still is, a peasant or traditional business on a very small scale in some countries. Traditional oils are worth their weight in gold. Sheer liquid sunshine or energy!

Understanding the crudest technology allows us to see the pitfalls and advantages of more advanced technology, but at the end of the day the process is simple. I have observed women in Morocco milling and grinding Argan seeds by hand to obtain the multi-purpose precious oil for cooking, heating, lighting, health and beauty. Just down the road is the mass-producing factory. The difference in the end product, in terms of taste, aroma, colour, and texture, is quite amazing. Traditionally Argan seeds should be first consumed by goats and then collected from their droppings to make the seeds easier to handle. Readers can draw their own conclusions!

The traditional way is to find a seed that easily yields oil. The seed is then pounded or crushed between two stones by hand or animal traction. The crushing effect combined with friction makes the oil yield, or run. It is hard work. Hard work and friction equals heat. Heat, as we have seen, is the enemy of quality oil. Try it yourself, if you like, with a pestle and mortar. It's not easy and will emphasise the point that some seeds and nuts are easier to work with than others. These easy ones are the traditional oil crops like olive; it is almost as though Nature intended them to be used. Now we can see that some raw materials may require more heat or pressure to give up any oil at all, and if so, then it might get 'cooked', be tar-like, and so require refining to be usable.

Consider also that the process might not be just to produce oil. Oils are very much part of the detergent or soap industry. They are also part of the paint, solvent, and even cattle food industries. So we have to be aware of the type of material that we want to use or end up with. Some mills work for food grade oils; to others, this is almost a by-product.

Consumers often see themselves these days as 'green' people, not politically speaking, but soft on Nature, with a feeling that natural does you good. Whether an oil is for ingestion or external use, it would be right to say that such consumers are looking for a product as near to Nature as is possible. They, and ethical practising therapists, would want a full content of vitamins, fatty acids, etc. (The essential fatty acids were once known as vitamin F.) It is not really an argument about what academics or doctors may say cannot go through the skin, or that it's physiologically impossible for an oil to benefit a person in a certain way. These arguments, and there are two sides, hide the rights of the public to have what they want and the right of the therapists to use what they want. It is the right of the therapist to say what is best for them to use by experience. Holistic therapists have always said they want to be, and use materials that are, as near to Nature as is possible. This is not the province of legislation that will always back the mass producer, but a matter of information and, based upon this, freedom of choice. If people want to behave in a so-called unscientific way, then surely it is their freedom of choice to do so.

This desire has to be, however, tempered with fact, reality and education. Whilst I do not quarrel with the sentiment, indeed I think I spawned the phrase 'as near to Nature as possible', it is not always practical. To start with, the purpose has to be clear. The quality must fit the situation.

The question as to what is really possible has to be asked and answered as well. An unrefined oil is not always best; semi-refined or refined may suit one situation and not another. This is particularly true if making massage oils, creams or lotions that are meant to last more than, say, three months. If it is living, it is dyeing; and sometimes near-to-Nature products decompose quickly – that's the way of Nature. Nature not only abhors a vacuum but it also has to build up or break down.

The answers to these questions indicate that people must have a good relationship with a supplier or a brand that provides a lot of detail. Aromatherapy, in its infancy, has been subject to a lot of get–rich-quick merchants. They will sell anything; they will sell you 'what you want'. The label says it's natural and unrefined, and that may be true, but it may also be rancid and full of free radicals! Hardly the best for treatment!

Let's move on to general industrialised processing and look at common features. At the beginning, the seed has to be cleaned to remove stones, dirt, metal parts from broken machinery, animal droppings, or a dead mouse or two! Obviously part of this process is to de-shell or husk the seed. This is done with a variety of vibrating sieves, belts and magnets. After the cleansing, the seed is normally broken up between rollers to provide flattened flakes, meal, or flour.

At this point the oil bearing meal is usually placed into a heating vessel or kettle, and is cooked a little. The heat in the vessel expands the oil and moisture in the minute seed cells which burst open, partially releasing the oil into the meal. This is called **pre-heating** and takes place between 45° and 85°C (110°-180°F). Temperature is very important at this stage as the all-important fatty acids in cis form are temperature sensitive.

After the heating or kettling, the oil-bearing material is moved to the expeller, which may be heated or unheated (cold press). *All* expellers or mills generate *heat*, even hand grinding, so cold-pressing can mean different things. We must remember that the friction heat generated with a high volume processor will be between 70° - 85°C (160° - 185°F). The expeller is basically a powerful screw that squeezes (compresses) the cooked seed, thus producing oil. The higher the speed and pressure, the higher the temperature.

This oil may then go straight to the filter and would be considered the best quality oil coming from a high volume producer. It may be referred to as 'virgin cold pressed', or something similar, as no *extra* heat was used in the press or expeller.

Many, if not all, oils are treated in this way. A very few, such as Sunflower, Olive, or Sesame, may go through a simple press. Most do not. In general terms the idea of an old fashioned mill slowly pressing away is romantic fiction. They do exist, but rarely – it's usually stainless steel and mass production! We can see that a cold press does not mean refrigerated or even room temperature. Mechanical work means the production of heat. Never think that 'cold pressed' means a man with a hammer pounding seeds into a filter, or a donkey – or even a camel – turning a grind stone. You would have to look hard to find such material in a retail environment. The friction heat in an expeller can generate very high temperatures. At high temperatures, reactions speed up. For every $10°C$ temperature rise, the rate of reactivity doubles.

Let's return to the process and reconsider the residual meal now turned to a pulp. There is still a lot of oil left within the pulp. The pulp, having gone through a screw press, is obviously much more solid. It is now in a cake form so it has to be broken up again, flaked, and is then taken for solvent extraction.

The method of solvent extraction is variable, but basically a petroleum mixture or a solvent like hexane is sprayed over moving trays until the point at which the concentration of oil within the solvent is great enough for the solvent to be evaporated and distilled away. The solvent is then available to be re-used and the oil is pumped away, sometimes to rejoin the original material from the expeller. Sometimes super-heated steam may be used as a solvent to force out more oil from the cake pulp.

Filtration to remove any residues concludes the oil mill process. It describes the way better quality oils are produced. All the oils so far can be described as crude. They are all *near to Nature* in so far as they are still unrefined, but already we can see a distinction in terms of production quality. What is the heat of the cold press? Do you want a solvent extracted oil or blended oil? Price becomes a fair indicator.

It is true that a small number of simple presses or expellers exist, but these are decreasing in Europe, not increasing. Some of these specialist mills only work with organic produce, and so maintain a premium for their product. Special expellers at high quality mills run at temperatures of only 47-50° C. In Switzerland and France you will find regulation that governs the temperature of a cold press at 50 or 60° C maximum. For the rest, it's potluck. Paying the premium price for such oils maintains these small mills that can only exist on the basis of a discerning, appreciative user.

Olive Oil is the oft-quoted source for traditional production, but in the 70's and 80's, centrifuge plants began to replace the presses. Tourists rarely see these, just the old-fashioned presses that are often maintained to keep up an illusion. These are the tourist Museums found in the growing areas. The centrifuge method increases productivity but reduces the natural antioxidants such as cafeic acid. Such lost substances not only provide stability but also provide health benefits.

The oil mill is not the same as the refinery. They are not always in the same plant or location. Crude oil travels the world. It is only after milling, when the crude is produced, that the refining process can begin. Refining can take the form of neutralising, bleaching, filtering, and deodorising, fully or incompletely.

The very word 'refined' sounds better than 'crude'; it sounds like an improvement. Indeed it can be, depending upon what you want to do. It can also provide a disaster in the wrong area of activity. The refining process covers a number of operations all of which, or only some of which, may take place. Some are simple, like carbon filtering, and others are more aggressive. It all depends upon the processor, and treatments can vary considerably. Oil needs to be refined as much for storage purposes as for any other.

You will be familiar with the concept "If it's living, it's dyeing," especially if you have attended my lectures on the Quality of Essential Oils. The refining process aids storage, but taken to its ultimate conclusion, it could be said to remove or destroy all the life sustaining nutrients. It's the story of the cooking oil that never goes off! The ideal for most cosmetic manufacture is something odourless, colourless and stable.

One of the first processes is neutralising the oil, especially if the end use is an edible mass cooking oil. This is particularly relevant if the starting material was of poor quality, perhaps even partially degraded. Chemical changes take place if material is not stored or harvested properly. Some fatty acids are not bound to glycerol and are free. These would contribute to decomposition. The whole process is to fully utilise oils to maximise profit. In effect the more components you can extract, the more you can resell at better margins.

Neutralising is also part of the soap-making industry. In the removal of the natural free fatty acids, an alkali such as caustic soda is floated through the oil. The process involves heating and stirring. The acids and soda combine to form a soap which sinks to the bottom of the tank and the 'purified' oil is then run off where it is washed several times with hot water. The waste is sold off as 'soap stock'.

Following this will come the bleaching, which can be done with a simple method involving Fuller's Earth or carbon, or something more aggressive. To give some idea of the volumes we are talking about, we are maybe looking at a tank of at least 50 tonnes. Discolouration or bleaching may sometimes be desirable, especially for the paint industry. The mantra of marketing men and women is that cooking oil should all look the same on the shelf. Carotenes (vitamins) contribute a yellow colour and part of the benefit of the plant. Chlorophyll quickly oxidises from a good green to a brown, unpleasant, smelly liquid. Sometimes a synthetic molecule with a copper content is added to keep the colour green.

So colour is best removed if storage is expected. The process is usually done by clay, carbon or silica absorption, a relatively straightforward 'discoloration' process. Natural waxes, which make an oil look cloudy in cool conditions, are eliminated by 'winterisation.' When cooled, the waxes crystallise and they are then separated by filter or centrifuge. This stops the oil going cloudy when cold. (If they do go cloudy generally take this as a good sign!)

Bleaching is often undertaken because it is said that consumers do not like the natural colours of the oil or because the material is destined for the paint or varnish industry. Bleaching or discoloration can be carried out with an edible oil in mind or not. If for food or real Aromatherapy, and if deemed really necessary then the use of Fullers Earth or charcoal are the preferred means for simple discoloration. For other purposes, chemicals that liberate chlorine or oxygen may be used. The former takes time and is expensive compared to chemical bleaching. The actual colouring matter is physically removed. The alternative is to destroy the colouration by oxidation with a resultant residue. In practice many chemical methods may be used, sulphuric acid, manganese dioxide and so on.

One has to realise that these processes remove virtually all of the vitamin E, lecithins, carotenoids, and chlorophylls; but worse still, one may be converting the fatty acids into the toxic trans fatty acids. It will all depend upon the plant and process. Generalisations are just that. Actual results will depend upon the acidity of the bleaching earth as well as temperature.

The deodorising phase is very relevant to us because whilst it can be simple, such as carbon filtering, mostly the oil is subjected to a superheated steam treatment at temperatures as high as 230°-260° C (around 445°-500° F). It's a type of distillation. The worst thing about this is that the company may be selling the product as a low temperature or cold pressed oil, which it may have been, but ignoring or failing to label any further processing. The odorous substances are swept away leaving fairly neutral oil. At 200° C, real and damaging changes occur. Trying to find such information from manufacturers can be difficult, often hidden by trade confidentiality and so on.

Now, one more process may take place. This is hydrogenation or the hardening of the liquid oil into a hard fat, what we would now call margarine. As noted, a great deal of heat and pressure are required, as well as a reaction with hydrogen gas and metal catalysts – nickel, or even platinum. Naturally hard fats are 'safe' in the sense that they contain no trans fatty acids to interfere with essential fatty acid activity in the body. Process-hardened fats are not the same thing at all. A little real butter that your digestion recognises is probably not such a bad idea.

Most of us are familiar with the partially hardened fats, which do contain large numbers of trans fatty acids. What do trans fatty acids actually do?

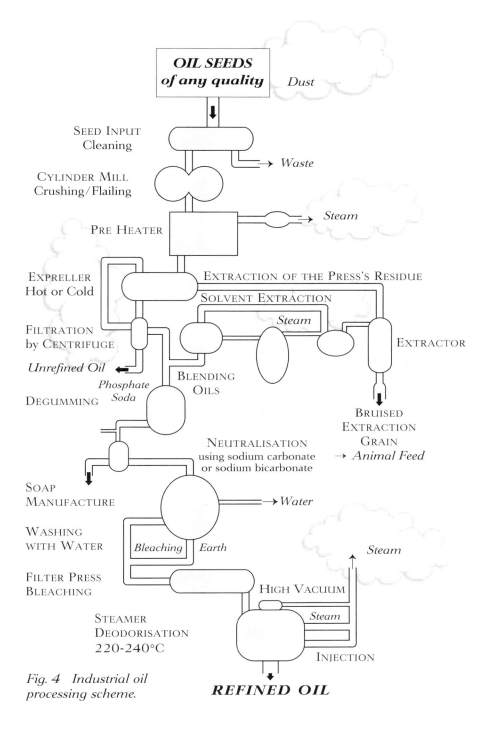

OIL SEEDS
of any quality          *Dust*

SEED INPUT
Cleaning

→ *Waste*

CYLINDER MILL
Crushing/Flailing

PRE HEATER          → *Steam*

EXTRACTION OF THE PRESS'S RESIDUE
EXPRELLER
Hot or Cold

SOLVENT EXTRACTION
*Steam*

FILTRATION
by CENTRIFUGE          EXTRACTOR

*Unrefined Oil*

BLENDING
*Phosphate*    OILS
DEGUMMING    *Soda*

BRUISED
EXTRACTION
GRAIN
→ *Animal Feed*

NEUTRALISATION
using sodium carbonate
or sodium bicarbonate

SOAP
MANUFACTURE          → *Water*

WASHING
WITH WATER          *Steam*

*Bleaching*    *Earth*

FILTER PRESS
BLEACHING          HIGH VACUUM

*Steam*

STEAMER
DEODORISATION
220-240°C          INJECTION

*Fig. 4  Industrial oil
processing scheme.*          **REFINED OIL**

In the book *Fats That Heal, Fats That Kill*, one of the world's experts on the subject, Udo Erasmus, puts it this way:

> "Trans fatty acids compete for enzymes, produce biologically non functional derivatives, and interfere with the work of the essential fatty acids in the body. Because of our association with the word 'poly unsaturates' with health we are fooled into thinking that we are buying a health-giving product of good quality, a product that is actually health destroying."

Another quotation, this time from Professor Bisson, Professor of Nutrition at Laval University in Quebec says:

> "It would be practically impossible to predict with accuracy either the nature or the content of these new molecules (produced by hydrogenation). Between the parent vegetable oil, sometimes labelled 'pure,' and the partially hydrogenated product there is a world of chemistry that alters profoundly the composition and physiochemical properties of natural oils. Herbert Dutton, an oil chemist of some reputation in the United States, says 'If the hydrogenation process were discovered today it would probably not be adopted by the oil industry.' He adds 'The basis for such comment lies in the recent awareness of our prior ignorance concerning the complexity of isomers formed during the hydrogenation and their metabolic and physiological fates.'"

All this refining and processing is a far cry from what we set out to achieve – which was something as near to Nature as is possible. Perhaps what we would like to see is just a process such as seed cleaning, husking, then a movement back to direct, small batch cold-pressing – no further processing, no heat treatment, and packages in dark glass to stop light oxidation. Of course, this would mean that we are looking at a much more expensive oil because companies are losing all the profit that would have been derived from the refining process, but it would be alive and as near to Nature as is possible. It would also mean a change in shopping habits, even lifestyle. The ideal of returning to small farms and small processors seems a romantic dream at the beginning of the new millennium.

In fairness, this latter route is not always practicable and possible, and you have to decide yourself which parameters you will apply. For example, some oils are virtually impossible to obtain and use fresh because they go off so quickly. So, within the terms of the refining, we may have to accept some compromises for certain oils, whereas with other oils we can find exactly what we want in a relatively unprocessed form. Experience is an important factor. Theory is fine but Nature does not always do what we expect.

Economics and the source material play parts in choosing materials. Only a very few oils, such as Olive Oil, are edible straight from the mill. The first cold pressed oil uses about five kg of green olives to make one kg of oil. All other seeds and nuts are subject to some processing if destined for consumption, for a variety of reasons including the presence of toxins generated during storage. Whilst oils do not support bacterial growth, they are prone to certain micro-organic growth such as moulds.

Being practical and realistic, you have to decide for what purpose you want to use your vegetable oil. You may accept one quality of oil for your medicinal purpose as it is to be used quickly, and quite another for a product which goes into a cosmetic that has to live in hot conditions on a hot shelf for three years.

## Crude, Virgin or Refined?

You will by now see that there is no simple answer to the question of what is best. The intended purpose is paramount. Whilst I subscribe to the basic philosophy of *organic, crude, virgin*, I cannot impose this view or clearly justify it in every external use. Matters are a little more straightforward with ingestion.

'The whole is greater than the sum of its parts' is the dictum of holistic thought. It is the idea of synergy, as promoted since the 1960's. Much effort in dietary advice is based upon analysis claiming that one source is as good as another in terms of chemistry. People, however, seem to have some substances that suit them better than others. This should not be overlooked. Whole oils, say crude or unrefined, are potentially packed with synergistic materials. Very little work about this has been taken forward with skin care, which in medical terms is a bit of a Cinderella. Vegetable oils unfortunately do not rate highly enough in most materia medica.

Vegetable oils have practical uses, but they are also part of the food, cosmetic and pharmaceutical industries. Exotic oils like andiroba, babassu, monoi and tamanu, all tell their own tale of faraway delights. This touch of the mysterious and luxurious may have little bearing on practical application and results, they can simply be fashions. If an oil transits halfway round the world, then it is likely to need some stabilisation or change to its nature to be usable.

The terms 'crude', 'virgin' and 'refined' are, to say the least, hazy. The *best* quality is not always what we expect. Oils are obtained from nuts, seeds and occasionally pulp or fruit seed, as in olive or avocado. 'Crude' simply refers to the end material or oil of the extraction process itself, whereas the term 'refined' indicates further processing or industrialisation. The term 'virgin' is applied to a type of crude oil.

Crude means unrefined. It does not mean process-free. Crude oil, or its starting material, will have been at least cleansed, dried, shelled, crushed, sometimes heated to sterilise or to deactivate natural enzymes, pressured and filtered. Virgin oils are crude oils obtained by mechanical process. Production should be at an appropriate temperature to maintain the components in an unaltered state. Crude virgin oils are more or less supposed to be preserved by the antioxidants they naturally contain. The shelf life, as we have seen, will depend upon the type and number of fatty acids, the number of double bonds and the nature of the few extra components in the oil, such as natural antioxidants, and the conditions in which they are stored. For sure, you will find a lot of information about the crude oil being used to describe its refined partner.

When buying specialist oils, it's a worthwhile exercise to check up on the storage facilities of your supplier. Some companies operate virtually from garden sheds and back rooms. Internet sites are notorious for disguising poor

*Mixture of common nuts. Note the shape of the walnut kernels.*

*Rape fields – the bane of the British countryside*

*Palm trees, near Tunis, Tunisia*

*Coconut trees and nuts*

*Vegetable oils come in many colours: pale yellow to green or even red.*

*Borage growing in Finland*

*Olive oil production. Small producers still exist.*

*Cold pressed oil – liquid energy from the sun*

resources behind multi-media displays. Some suppliers have open barrels and large headspace in large volume containers, a sure way of encouraging degradation. They may store in the wrong type of plastic container. Look for the suppliers who store under nitrogen, and when you acquire good oils use them quickly when opened. Sometimes extra antioxidant is added, usually natural or synthetic vitamin E, tocopherol, which is found naturally in Wheatgerm Oil.

## COMMON TERMS FOUND ON LABELS

**Virgin** – Oil obtained solely by mechanical means and supposedly where heating has not altered the oil.

**Extra Virgin** – A difficult term to imagine! Selected for taste and odour. When applied to Olive Oil, an acidity of less than 1%.

**Fine Virgin** – This term allows for higher acid values to 1.5%

**Semi-Fine** – Acid values of 3% are allowed. This is the 'normal' or ordinary oil.

**Virgin Lampante** – A term used for Olive Oil. High acid values. Lamp oil destined for the refinery or industry but does find its way to Aromatherapy as it is cheap.

**Refined** – Covers a multitude of possibilities. Acid values adjusted etc., and certainly possible from virgin oil.

**Pure** – Indistinct term that may mean a blend of virgin and refined.

**Residue** – A term you are unlikely to see. It is solvent extraction oil from spent, cold pressed materials and is destined for industrial use, commercial cooking and cosmetic oils.

The question of refining is very relevant to the starting material – the nuts, seeds, and fruit. If the original material was not fit for human consumption, was old, deteriorating, fermenting, even larvae or worm-ridden, then harmful elements such as moulds or yeasts may contaminate the resulting oil. Good almonds are best for eating, chocolatiers and cake makers! Bacteria, as stated, are not supported by oil but other toxins may be. This is why, if you buy crude or virgin oil, you should buy the best.

Over one hundred years ago it was recognised that there were other components to oils, other materials called glycerides, vitamins, unsaponifiable fractions and unwanted matter such as moulds and the aflatoxins. Moulds that grow on nuts and seeds are potential carcinogens and can cause liver damage. Today we rightly show concern about pesticides or other residues that may be present. Other components are a matter of so-called consumer preference, like waxes, which go cloudy in the cold. (Alternatively, if consumers want a whole oil – this is a quality plus). Water can be present and be an instability factor. Natural free fatty acids in particular are very prone to oxidation.

So refining is carried out, not only for economic reasons, but also to reduce some of the aforementioned problems. Some refining processes are less harsh than others. Refining has a role depending upon the purpose – some oils need to undergo some refinement to make them usable.

Not every seed is commonly used for human consumption. Grape pips, cherry stones and the seeds found in Rose Hips (not the pulp) come under this category. Such materials by their very nature require some special industrial processing to make them useful at all.

Perhaps Olive Oil has a privileged place, along with Avocado, Palm, and Coconut. Few starting crops yield oil so easily as these. Olive Oil, due to its status, has particular European standards. They have been in force since 1959, although since amended and updated. For the average user it is the easiest oil to begin with as an appreciation test. Some stores run these now, similar to wine tasting. Once you appreciate the differences in oils, as with essential oils, 'the penny drops' about quality and the fine things of life. If you are going to pay a lot of money for treatment, say at some special spa, then you have every right to demand and expect the best. It makes a difference to you and the benefit you derive, but might stretch the budget of the brand or hotel that will invariably buy cheapest. You deserve more!

If you want real benefit rather than a holiday massage, the caring independent therapist might be the best bet for finding real quality. Check out what oils they are using and be prepared to pay the extra. Big brands will demand bigger profit and may well cut quality in meeting the needs of the shareholders demand for increasing profit.

Refining may have a combined end result undertaken in one plant for different industries. We have briefly touched on this when discussing making margarines. Soap or detergent manufacture may be the goal or end market for run offs. Certain oils are best for this process and so, as you can imagine, there are specialising refineries or specialist processes for this huge industry. Another name for soap making is saponification.

Sometimes you will notice that oils are given a SAP or saponification value. This a simple measure of how much potassium hydroxide in milligrams is needed to make soap from one gram of any particular oil. Conversely you will also find a measure of the unsaponifiables, this is shown on Safety Data Sheets. Each oil has a SDS (Safety Data Sheet) for the benefit of industrial processors. Sometimes hospital pharmacies like to have them, but in truth they are of little use for practical purposes outside industry. What applies to handling huge volumes may not be significant when handling a few grams. Literally, this unsaponifiable measure is what it says – the content of things that will not react with an alkali to form soap. From the soap maker's point of view, these are impurities; but as they include the all-important vitamins, sterols, etc., they can be reclaimed and resold at extra profit through the supplement industry.

If the objective is to make soap, several steps have to be taken. The fatty acids have to be separated from the glycerol or glycerine. When acids react with metals, salts are formed. The fatty acid content of an oil will react with a metal to form a salt we call 'soap'. Hydroxides are used; sodium produces a hard soap, and potassium produces a soft soap. Of course this is an extreme simplification but it allows us to see the versatility of the vegetable oils.

We have mentioned that in oil refining one of the objectives is to make a neutral oil by removing the free fatty acids. Neutralisation with soda is most common. Soap making allows even degraded or deteriorating material to be used. Acids and alkali are combined whilst heating and agitating the material in a vessel. The soap sinks to the bottom of a vat or tank and is run off. The leftover oil is then washed with hot water several times to remove all traces of soaps and alkalis. Any excess water is removed in a spray tower at around 90° C. This is how soap stock is made.

Of course whilst soaps and detergents are different in common idiom, they all clean things. They do the same thing even if they have different properties or origins – for example soap doesn't work in hard water whereas a detergent does. The example of soap making also allows us to begin to glimpse the relationship between names we see on detergent, shampoo and washing up liquid bottles, names such as 'lauryl sulphate'. Lauric acid, a main fatty acid constituent of Coconut and Palm oils, is a favourite of the detergent manufacturer. Hence we often see on detergent bottles, 'coconut derived' or similar phrases. Of course chemically and 'naturally' we have come a long way from a coconut, but surely these are better materials than those drawn from the petrochemical industry. Why? At the very least they are drawn from a renewable resource that will provide continuous management and employment.

Of course to every process there are downsides and/or side-effects. It is up to each individual to draw a line based upon current knowledge. Rational education is the key to progress, not hype and the claims of dubious experts with their names attached to specific brands. For example, vegetable-based detergents have been associated with cancer when applied to the skin. You now know that all oils have an acid base. Irritations can cause cancer. It's hardly surprising that a great mental leap can link the two. The possibility is there, but what about the probability, the risk benefit factors, dilution rates, biodegradability, individual reaction, the balance between freedom of choice and over restrictive legislation based on political correctness. The informed therapist helps the client and patient to make a sound and reasoned choice.

Industrialisation and refining have given us other measures that are applied to fats. The 'Iodine value' gives the measure of saturation. Saturated fats have low iodine values and unsaturated fats have higher iodine values. This is useful to people wanting a hard soap or stiff emulsion. Sweet Almond has a value of 105, Kukui 165; and at the other end of the spectrum, Coconut has a value of 10.

The 'Peroxide value' is a good indicator of whether an oil is aged or not, and its likelihood of going rancid. The higher the peroxide value, the more troublesome it is to store the oil.

Free Fatty acids are also commonly measured. These, as we have discussed, are a major cause of rancidity and are present in crude oils. The arguments for and against their removal are clear and, as I have put forward, purpose and storage are part of the equation of choice. The choice also depends upon the oil. It would be hard to justify using a crude Rose Hip Seed Oil, with its propensity to degeneration, as an active in a therapeutic situation. The removal of free fatty acids by making a soap has been described above. The acid value is the percentage of free fatty acids present in the oil.

Free fatty acids not only give off odours but also contribute to the natural odour of the oil, the recognisable smell of the nut. Deodorisation is performed by dry steam carrying the volatile odour substances away under high vacuum and at high temperature. You will need to decide if you want a massage oil with a distinctive nut oil aroma, maybe conflicting with your own blend, or whether you want a neutral oil.

Working with crude material is more consistent with the authenticity of the holistic or natural approach. However, as some crude oil may be produced by solvent extraction, there may be a desire to use virgin oil, which may not be available for the plant seed species, you want to use. So you either limit yourself to a few good oils, or you make a point of compromise.

Most measures found on specification sheets are designed for industry. They tell us little of practical value for use in the home, clinic or salon.

It can now be understood that oils vary tremendously from supplier to supplier. Pure 'X' named Oil may be a blend of virgin with refined. Flavours, colours, smells – all can be specified. An example is common grapeseed, which, in its 'natural' or crude state, can be black, and tarry – only refinement makes it usable. Is this what a holistic therapist wants? Using a different process may yield a very different product, though both grapeseed in origin. Similarly, Light Coconut Oil, which is highly refined, has little in common with Coco-butter or Coprah Oil. The purpose has to be considered alongside technology and philosophy.

What should be clear to the purchaser, therapist or client is the nature of the material being used. A little extra price often brings its own reward. In cosmetics, rather than therapeutic Aromatherapy, virgin or crude oils are more difficult to handle, and is inappropriate for mass marketing in many cases. The working therapist can therefore offer something better than the potted version of the department store, provided they obey the rules and work with an ethic.

## The Price of Organics

Haven't we put the cart before the horse here? Whilst discussing oils, little reference has been made to the quality of the starting material except in passing with relevance to possible contamination, etc. Organic agriculture is becoming more popular. In the mind of the public, 'Organic' means grown without the use of synthetic chemical herbicides, pesticides or fertilisers. Whilst true, this is an oversimplification. Organic agriculture tries, to a certain degree, to replicate natural *soil* conditions. It is strictly speaking about increasing sustainable agriculture without high inputs, and the maintenance of soil fertility.

It is quite possible and desirable to use oils from organically grown nuts and seeds. This, of course, limits choice and you will normally pay a much higher price for Organic material than standard products. Consumers do not like this, and unfortunately even therapists complain. Due to supermarket popularity, farmers are coming under the same kind of severe price pressure that has already put so many non-organic farmers out of business. Supermarkets may be great places to shop but their trendy buyers and specifiers are definitely not Nature's friends. Prices need to be at a level that reflects the true cost of production. If they are not, Organic farming will always be a fringe activity. Society must stop its obsessive love affair with cheapness. Quality cannot be obtained by cut price.

In the 16th century, the philosopher Francis Bacon urged mankind to "Conquer and subdue her (Mother Nature)… And make her your slave." We seem to have done a good job but, as with all slavery, at a price we later find we cannot afford! We have to change our thinking. Nature *and* society are still suffering from the Age of Enlightenment that set the pattern for a materialistic society. Organic agriculture suffers the taint of being vitalistic, the belief in the maintenance of life force, philosophy rather than science. Times are changing, and so is the vocabulary. As Physics shows us, there is more to life than Chemistry.

I am passionate about buying Organic for many reasons. For example, cheap produce – be it potato or oil – is very costly. An average UK family in 2001 paid the government £16 a week in farming subsidies and a further £11 a week to put right the environmental damage from non-organic farming. We spend millions on health and do little to support ourselves through good nutrition. We spend millions on home entertainment and complain about the price of carrots that, if non-organic, may poison us – but they must be cheap. In the 1970's we spent 24% of our household budget on food; today that has sunk to 16%, and this allows for the relative expense of processed products, the consumption of which has increased dramatically.

So why are organics more expensive in the stores and, perhaps even more so if you deal with specialist mail-order suppliers? The European Union pays subsidies from taxpayers that favours intensive farming, giving a distorted production cost. In addition, Prof. Jules Pretty estimates £2.3 billion a year goes on clean up and clear up costs. It takes at least two years for a farm to be converted to Organic, with a consequent loss of income and no premium price since the produce is not organic until the period is complete. During the conversion period, new training, equipment and investment in soil fertility will cost money. Non-intensive farming is just that, so yields may drop. Crop rotation means that up to 25% of farm space may be given over to building soil fertility rather than crop production. Biodiversity is a constituent part of the system so wildlife will have to be managed; this too is a cost. Seeds are more expensive as traditional varieties are not grown to the scale of intensive producers. Organic farming requires more labour and less mechanisation. The use of husbandry rather than agrochemicals requires good staff and training. Organic agriculture is not a cheap method of production, but production methods are only part of the story. A lot can happen to an organic sunflower seed between farm and therapist! Many other quality parameters apply.

Using Organic material will cut choice, but are all these oils needed? Could we not manage with just a dozen at most? Undoubtedly yes. I have already raised the point of difference between, say, nuts that yield an oil by simple pressure, and seeds that require enormous heat, pressure or even solvents to give up an oil. It cannot be right that we were created to rely upon essential fatty acids available only to us by technology, and fashionable seeds clearly not eaten by our ancestors. Many oils are no more than the use of waste by other industries, the classic example being grape pips. Not such a bad thing in itself, but their processing is questionable and their value is pure assumptive chemistry. It seems only yesterday that all margarine was good and all butter was bad – now we have a more balanced view.

In Aromatherapy and body care, cosmetics and toiletry fashion plays a major role. Most manufacturers are not looking for activity at all, except perhaps for common action like an oil film. The true reason for use is that a little Kiwi Seed Oil is a lot more exciting than Sunflower, unless of course we can get Organic Sunflower…organic is fashionable…But can we get the supply price down…can we get the consumer to pay a premium…Umm, food for thought!

# 5

# *Benefits in Skin Care and Nutrition*

F<sub>ats</sub> or oils are major components of cell walls, intracellular membranes. These are typically made up of a double layer of phospholipids. Cholesterol, so often painted as the bad guy, is fundamental to such membranes. It's not surprising that oil is important in skin care.

Aromatherapy, perhaps the leading proponent these days of topical applications of oils and fats, also takes dietary concerns into consideration. In particular the vitamin, mineral, and fatty acid status of an individual are of importance to well-being, health and beauty. Cosmetic houses, too, have started to put forward skin care regimes that provide supplements specific to skin care. Many of these are based upon essential fatty acids.

The skin itself contains a number of fats and related substances. You would expect to find the following in 'average' skin fats:

| | |
|---|---|
| Triglycerides | 32% |
| Free fatty acids | 28% |
| Waxes | 14% |
| Cholesterol and esters | 4% |
| Squalene | 5% |
| Other hydrocarbons | 8% |
| Steroids | 9% |

Vegetable oils provide, at the very least, emollient properties to the skin. They are among the oldest used health and cosmetic materials known to mankind. They are regularly used and chosen because of their low incidence of irritation, sensitisation and comedogenicity. They feel good for the skin and are good for the skin. Moisturising and skin softening are basic uses for oils.

The body produces its own protective oil that we call 'sebum', a mixture of fatty acids and glycerides. Sebum is produced from special glands that are controlled by hormones, and are most active after puberty. As people get older the production of this perfectly natural moisturiser decreases. People with Mediterranean or more oil-prone skin appear to age less quickly than those with drier skins, provided they keep away from long sun exposure.

The natural replacement is vegetable oils. Some oils are absorbed more quickly than others. Some oils are thicker than others, especially the saturated materials – Coconut, for example – and we may even call them greasy to the touch. Medium touch oils are usually monounsaturated, such as Avocado, Almond, Olive, and Sesame. Sunflower Oil has mainly poly-unsaturated fats, as does Walnut. These are the thinner oils.

Our skin has two basic layers. The outer layer is called 'the epidermis', the deepest layer of which produces new living skin cells termed 'keratinocytes'. These cells are named after the tough, insoluble protein called 'keratin'. These skin cells are constantly being pushed upward toward the surface. As they rise, they lose effective life but produce what we see and call our skin. This top surface is called the 'stratum corneum'. It is a dry, protective zone composed of dead and dyeing cells. The inner layer, 'the dermis', is a network of protein fibres such as collagen and elastin, connective tissues that form the bulk of our body. Below, and integrated within this network, lay the blood vessels needed to bring nutrients to the germinative point, the granular layer where new keratinocytes are formed. There are a multitude of glands, nerves and sensors buried in the dermis.

The stratum corneum is the part of the epidermis or skin that is in contact with the environment. It's our contact with the outside world. Not only does it reflect us and our health, but it also has to take everything the environment and our lifestyle throws at it. As we know, it is made up of layers of totally keratinised cells, separated by intercellular space occupied by lipids. The lipids themselves form lamellar bi-layers. The main lipids found in this area are called 'ceramides'. The same substances can be found in cereal

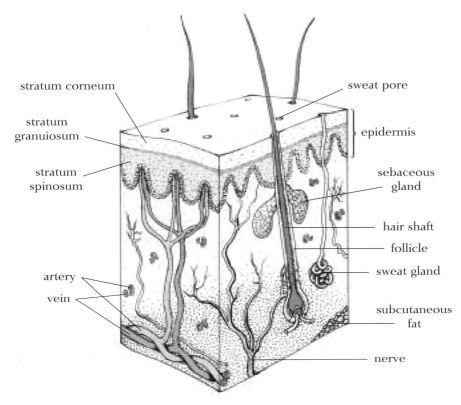

stratum corneum

stratum granuiosum

stratum spinosum

artery

vein

sweat pore

epidermis

sebaceous gland

hair shaft

follicle

sweat gland

subcutaneous fat

nerve

*Fig. 5.1   Diagram of skin structure.*

oils. So it's not so much a 'dead' area but an active one supporting the biological function of the skin. This multi-lamellar film structure is responsible for optimising the skin's moisture levels and providing a youthful, elastic aspect and form.

Collagen in the skin has strong moisturising and retentive powers. Collagen is therefore the responsible factor in providing plumpness or underlying smoothness, elasticity. Collagen will dehydrate when the lipidic barrier is poor or damaged. Such dehydration makes the skin look saggy. Look after the oil film, and collagen is maintained at its best.

As skin cells migrate to the surface they change shape, gradually emptying or flattening. We might reasonably ask why they do not fall off and expose the fresh cells. In fact they do. We shed skin cells regularly; much of the dust we see in a home can be made of shed skin cells! Fortunately we do not shed them all at the same time. They are held in place by an intercellular cement-like substance.

The intercellular 'cement' is composed of a mixture of body fluids that not only contribute to the appearance and texture of skin, but also plays a dynamic role in cell development. This 'cement' includes our old friends the phospholipids and fatty acids. Specialised sugars are also present together with amino acids. All these combine to make the skin a dynamic factory, and not just an envelope with a few well-defined activities. Sometimes we forget it is an organ that it obviously reflects our health.

The skin used to be thought of only as a 'barrier,' an envelope in which we live. Today we appreciate that it is both mechanically and biologically active. One of its extremely important but undervalued roles is to regulate moisture – the hydric flow.

On the skin surface is another forgotten layer perhaps more appropriately called a system. It is crucial to moisture retention, and is called the 'skin acid mantle'. This skin acid mantle is also vital to skin health; it is our first line of defence against germs, and is therefore a part of our defence system. It is formed not only as a mixture of sweat and sebum, but also by a colony of micro flora (bacteria) unique to each individual. This mantle is not only part of the defence system of the body, but also contains elements that maintain crucial moisture. Massaging with vegetable oils supports this crucial system.

## What vegetable oils are known to do

Standard orthodox textbooks still tell us that vegetable oils do not penetrate the skin. By and large this holds true. However if the skin is dry, oil will penetrate to the lowest optimum level. It becomes a moisturiser not only as a barrier to water loss, but by being bio available contributes to the natural moisturising factors of the skin even as a breakdown product of bio synthesis. It is supportive of skin activity. Molecular size should tell us that whilst essential oil molecules are small and therefore able to penetrate through the skin, oil molecules are too big. Nevertheless we term vegetable oils 'carriers', not just meaning that they hold or mix with essential oils in bottles but rather they carry essential oils into the skin. Essential oils are volatile; their nature is to go upward to the atmosphere not downward into skin. Sure, there are more complex reasons why essential oils travel to body systems, but in general terms we need to understand that when blended with vegetable oils they travel downward better!

As hinted already, certain oils are thicker or thinner. Logic might dictate that thinner oils penetrate more quickly. Each oil has a certain 'viscosity', a more accurate term than thick or thin. Viscosity is temperature dependent. So what is thick in a bottle might behave on warm skin in a different way, the classic example being Coconut Butter or Coprah Oil. In practice, Slavic Massage™ has shown that large volumes of a high viscosity oil blend can penetrate skin without leaving greasy deposits or an oily feel to the skin. Specially developed for this massage style, Slavic Massage Oil™ penetrates, in my opinion, because of the way it is applied. Over the years I have noted that the correct application of an oil aids absorption. This is clearly demonstrated at workshops.

Theory is fine but Nature is nonconformist! Science cannot see any obvious route that vegetable oils can be used beyond moisturisation. Yet shortly after the Second World War, as Leslie Kenton reports, Sunflower Oil was used to massage camp inmates in order to improve vitamin status (F) where the inmate's digestion could not cope with ingestion. Other cases of topical application have since that time shown this to be possible. Yet not all research confirms or can replicate this work. Aromatherapists, as classically the world's most extensive users of vegetable oils, in practice could well make more observations about this, perhaps working with dietary therapists or naturopathic practitioners.

Other improvements have been noted concerning essential fatty acid status when appropriate oils have been massaged. It could be reasoned that rather than assimilation through the skin, the skins own needs were met by localised metabolism or even by signals from communicant molecules allowing the body to fully utilise internally what was available to it by digestion. Rather than argue the point, it is good to recognise the value of oil massage.

It is a little similar to herbal oils where good results are reported when in theory the oil based material does not contain the active ingredients that should, in theory, supply the result. Many therapists report definitive results. Are they wrong simply because they contradict dogma that would deny their evidence? Are they telling stories? Is it the placebo effect? I do not think so. My own experience suggests that the skin is far more than we realise. Therapeutic touch combined with the memory of plants, vitalism if you like, provides a good solution. After all, what are all those nerves doing in our skin?

What cannot be dismissed is the value vegetable oils can display in treating difficult skin conditions. With or without essential oils, combinations of topically applied vegetable oils have been shown to be of value in difficult skin conditions such as eczema or psoriasis. This particularly applies to oils rich in Gamma Linoleic Acid.

Polyunsaturated oils are often rich in substances known as EFA's (essential fatty acids). They have this special term 'essential' because, unlike other fatty acids, they cannot be produced in the body, and because we need them to live and function. You could liken them to vitamins. It's crucial, therefore, that they are used at some point on the skin or taken as part of the diet. EFA's cannot be obtained except from outside our self so have special benefits for all manner of problems. One of the first signs of deficiency is a dry or flaky skin. The names to remember are confusingly similar. They are Linoleic and Linolenic acids.

As I mentioned in a previous chapter, once a double bond is present, the potential for different shapes in the molecule is also present. The same number and type of atoms are present but in a different arrangement. These types or shapes are called isomers and are named according to the Greek alphabet starting with alpha $\alpha$, beta $\beta$, gamma $\chi$, and so on. The more polyunsaturated the oil, the more potential there is for different isomers.

Linoleic acid has been identified in helping to lower cholesterol, maintaining moisture levels, and helping to build a better skin. Linolenic acid is present in a whole range of biological activities. It is needed to stimulate the production of gut bacteria, which in turn produce B vitamins vital to skin health. It, too, helps control cholesterol. These two fatty acids seem to work in synergy.

To help determine the differences between fatty acids and their applications, a further method of measurement was devised based upon the position of the double bond. The omega classification is a way of determining how far the carboxyl acid group –COOH- is from the first double bond. The number of carbons is counted *back toward* the carboxyl group. The number of double bonds is not considered in the system, only the first one being noted. The Greek alphabet, alpha to omega, is used; omega being the last letter and alpha the first, and alpha is taken as the carboxyl end. Nutritionists are concerned with the value of Omega 3, 6, and 9, sometimes written as Ω-3, Ω-6, and Ω-9. They say you need twice as much Omega 6 as 3. Classic examples of Omega 3 deficiency are dry skin, which must be of interest to all Aromatherapists.

The parent of the Omega 3 family of fatty acids is alpha Linolenic acid, whilst the Omega 6 family rises from Linoleic acid. Put them together, and you have activity that not only supports cell membranes, but is part of the formation of substances called 'prostaglandins'. These are hormone-like substances that control and regulate many body processes. Gamma Linolenic Acid (GLA), for example is the precursor of a particular prostaglandin series 1, which not only takes part in regulating the nervous and cardiovascular system but also skin condition or tone. Oleic acid, found in many oils but especially Olive Oil, gives the Omega 9 series. Though not essential, it is valuable as a hydrating material and conducive to a healthy regenerative system.

Omega 6 fats are converted by the body to gamma linolenic acid (GLA). GLA is converted into prostaglandins. GLA has much to do with blood pressure, blood thickness, and blood clotting, as well as nerve and immune functions. PMT, breast pain, and blood sugar problems can all be considered in relation to this oil and diet. The Omega 3 family are very readily damaged by heat and processing and so are more 'rare'. The best sources for this family are Hemp, Flax or Linseed, Pumpkin, and Melon oils, and, of course, the well-known Evening Primrose Oil.

A variety of skin conditions may benefit from ingestion or topical applications of different oils. Dry eczema and psoriasis may all be improved by the better utilisation of Omega 3 and Omega 6 oils. A combination of oils rich in these substances would be of practical benefit to those with a proneness to inflammatory health problems, loss of memory and/or hearing, and water retention. As has been stated, the eventual end-products from these fats are prostaglandins, which are essential for proper vision, learning, coordination, and mood.

## Looking at new possibilities

Following the menopause, certain fatty acids are found to reduce in older skin. As these constitute NMF's, or natural moisturising factors, it would be sensible to apply them at the site they are needed, right there in the skin, rather than by digestion. Specific in this instance would be palmitoleic acid from Macadamia Nut Oil, whilst lightness of touch may be supplied by blending with Apricot Kernel Oil. As the natural skin lipidic film is complex, it makes more sense to blend oils rather than simply using one oil. Several molecules and several active principles act in synergy. Of course, you could enjoy Macadamia nuts by eating them, and why not! Perhaps over indulgence?

As the skin condition deteriorates with age or due to stress it may become more sensitive, with the potential for irritation and disturbance in oil production or synthesis compounding the difficulty. Dry skin and atopical eczema typically always show up poor lipid barriers and low ceramide content in the epidermis.

In skin care, a sensitive or delicate skin is, by definition, an ultra dry skin. Dry skin is easily irritated or inflamed. Cold weather, central heating, and air conditioning all produce desert-like conditions for the skin. Oils are amazingly useful when applied to dry skin. Not everyone likes the feel of oil on the skin. Oils can be applied in different forms as emulsions such as lotions, creams or milks. Whenever you apply a cosmetic to the skin that has the appearance of cream or milk, it's an emulsion – a mixture of oil and water. The finest products can give the lightest texture or touch without the feeling of heaviness. These superb creams combine expertise in obtaining just the right mixture of oils, emulsifiers and waters, alongside specialist technology.

Cleansers can be made from vegetable oils, lifting out grime gently without aggression. Lecithin-rich oils are excellent for this job. We often talk about Roman baths, but the water part was for therapy and relaxation – the cleansing took place before the bath! The clean Roman was massaged with aromatic oils and literally scraped down for cleansing. Special spatulas were made to take off the dirt, dead skin cells and at the same time oil the body, a perfect form of exfoliation.

As we all know, the skin becomes drier and less elastic as we age; wrinkles form. This alteration in structure largely arises due to changes in the all-important lipidic or oil film. The composition of this film includes essential fatty acids, phospholipids and ceramides. It follows that blends of oils topically applied, and containing the right compounds, can only benefit the skin as it ages. The epidermis is capable of metabolising the elements necessary to recover its correct barrier function as well as looking its best. If you look good you probably are good!

Even oily skins can draw benefits from the application of vegetable oils. This is a heresy to many dermatologists. Aromatherapists have demonstrated the effectiveness. The theory goes like this. Over-production of sebum is sometimes a response to external aggression. These external causes of irritation or inflammation can have a variety of causes from dietary deficiencies to simple reactions to highly antiseptic soaps or harsh detergents. Unfortunately, oily skin is linked to impure or unclean. TV advertisements play this up, leading to a round of cleansing that in turn produces more oil. Often the target market is the teenage group where hormonal changes are often reflected in the skin.

Under these circumstances, if a light oil is used on its own or incorporated in an emulsion, perhaps with an essential oil or even better a floral water or hydrolat, the condition improves. The skin reduces its reaction of over-production because the stimulus or need is removed. The whole system is calmed down and returns to natural balance.

Although this book concentrates upon the topical use of oils in Aromatherapy or cosmetics, it would be good to review the process of the internal digestion of fats. Consumption and topical application both need, however, to be laid against the context of the orthodox path and so-called scientific thought It is normally held that a fat molecule is too large to penetrate the skin; however, it was not so long ago that the experts were decrying Aromatherapists when they said this did not always seem to be the case and that essential oils certainly could pass through the skin barrier. This, despite the fact that transdermal drug applications were coming into existence. Academia seems to hate new ideas coming from outside itself. Yet with all its resources in money and personnel, it can be a sterile place for ideas that are not wholly orthodox. Aromatherapy was only a few years ago something to be derided as childish nonsense. How could a smell have any effect upon disease! Aromatic molecules do not go through the skin and therefore have no effect! These were commonly held views.

Today all this has changed and research grants are being handed out for the 'New Scientific' discoveries in Smell Therapy and the new wonder Aromatic materials that can change the world. Poor old Aromatherapy has certainly missed the boat and the pioneers pushed to one side as Science now Speaks. As the European Union and other Medical Control Agencies seek to limit the natural freedom and right people have to exploit plant materials, the new grandees of the Aromatherapy profession want to move to become part of the establishment, recognised and respected. This will almost certainly kill off enterprise and freedom of choice, substituting for individual experience the double blind trial (often using the wrong materials), and standardised and industrialised material.

Likewise with vegetable oils, standardisation based upon the exploitation of safety issues is now the name of the game. Do we forget that safety is an industry like any other, an industry founded upon fear and distinctly biased toward the mass producer and supermarket retailers? These combine to limit choice, and to control our existence in a 'politically correct' society.

Vegetable oils and their derivatives do make news, for example Evening Primrose oil for PMT or Rose Hip seed oil as an anti-scar agent. Pick up any literature on alternative diets, and advocates of lecithin as an addition to the diet will soon be found. Pick up any standard orthodox textbook and hey presto, 'In the forms available in health food shops lecithin is useless as it is digested in the gut'! Never mind the fact that just a few years ago, when 'cranks' were saying you are what you eat and that dietary intake was important to health, hardly a medical man could be found to support this so-called new radical view. We can expect further shifts of long held views as new biology reassesses our own body systems and our relationship to the environment.

Nowadays we are given the impression we know all there is to know, such as that there is no difference between a synthetic vitamin and a natural one! I, for one, beg to differ. We generally claim to know everything about the mechanical human body, but just creeping around the edges these days are enlightened practitioners in the orthodox world who accept there is more to biology than the textbooks would have us believe. The skin and the nose, the very foundations of Aromatherapy, are being reassessed by science and the facts are coming out in favour of new metabolic pathways. It will not be long before some British, American or Japanese teaching hospital or university says it 'discovered' the whole world of Aromatherapy, including the beneficial use of vegetable oils applied externally, topically. Good skin care starts with good oils, applied properly, and reflects in a radiant look of health and well-being.

So leaving this context to one side, let's briefly review the accepted digestive route for fats. Please, however, keep in mind that what we put into our mouth – that which enters the lumen or gut – is not really inside us. The gut has an entrance and an exit; it is a large hole that goes right through us. It, too, is really a specialised skin, built to break down and then absorb the components. Bacteria inhabit this world and are vital to health, living in a symbiotic relationship with the self. This is, as we shall see, exactly the same as with our external organ, the skin.

In the gut, special enzymes get to work. The pancreas secretes a lipase that separates the fatty acids from glycerol. Bile produced by the liver and stored in the gall bladder is sent to the small intestine as an emulsifier needed to break down the components. Bile itself contains cholesterol. In the lining of the small intestine, changes occur that in turn re-synthesize these components back to minute particles that are transported by the blood stream.

As one oil may have more of one EFA or FA than another, blending oils and matching them to a purpose is sensible and useful. It's the skill of the trained Aromatherapist who recognises not only the value of the aromatics used, but also the bio-synergy produced when blended with active vegetable or herbal oils.

Oils can be taken as part of our diet. Nuts and seeds are the obvious source. What about salad dressing? Be adventurous. Almond Oil can be added to a dressing or dipped with bread as with Olive Oil. Sounds strange? It really isn't so different from spreading butter or another spread onto bread. Oils can be very delicious. Study the advantages of each oil type and use them to the full. When using them in cooking, go for taste and be judicious, remembering that heat just causes those trans forms and free radicals that age skin like nothing else.

It should be perfectly possible to improve the skin's health and appearance by topical applications of suitably balanced oil blends or complexes.

The Dermatological Archive in 1993 reported the following:

"Topical applications of individual lipids or incomplete mixtures of lipids interfere with barrier recovery, while complete mixtures of cholesterol, fatty acids, and ceramide allow normal barrier repair; and incomplete mixtures of topical lipids appear to inhibit barrier recovery at the level of the lamellar body resulting in abnormal intercellular membrane structures in the stratum corneum, abnormalities that do not occur when a complete lipid mixture is provided."

So get blending with whole oils.

Lipids account for about 14% of the total weight of skin. At the lowest levels the cells, keratinocytes, are principally surrounded by highly polar phospholipids and free fatty acids. At the granular layer, the keratinocytes are found to contain little organites called Odland bodies. It is here that the lipids of the stratum corneum will synthesise. The compositions of the intercellular lipids change so that cholesterol, ceramides and glycolipids can be found. Finally, in the topmost layers, cholesterol, free fatty acids and a special material called sphingolipid is released.

Cell reproduction or migration from base to surface also changes with age. Surface renewal is only fourteen days when young, but is double this by the time the age of fifty is reached. It makes sense to care for your skin as you get older. That care is provided for by the right *blend* of vegetable oils. The stratum corneum lipids are an approximate compound of 40% ceramides, 25% cholesterol, 25% free fatty acids, and 10% others.

Earlier, the term 'sphingolipids' was used as a generic term to which group ceramides belong. Skin ceramides are complex blends of hundreds of compounds, the function of which are quite unknown. Skin ceramides are highly saturated molecules and very stable; they do not go rancid easily.

Skin is not the simple tissue we often think it to be. We do not know all about it, and like the sense of smell, we are really only now getting to real grips with it. It is not yet understood why vegetable oils act on the stratum corneum previously considered 'dead' or inert. They could simply act as the missing lipids in order to simply reconstitute the missing or damaged bilayers. Other suggestions include the idea that the keratinocytes are fed by the oils and synthesise their own requirements from a starting material. Those with pronounced orthodox views treat such ideas with derision but orthodoxy has been wrong so many times. Certainly enzymatic reactions take place in the stratum corneum. The Odland bodies excrete glucosidase, an enzyme implicated in separating out ceramides.

Vegetable oils and their component compounds can have other benefits at enzymatic levels. The human leucocytary elastase is involved with inflammatory pathologies such as pulmonary emphysema, rheumatoid polyarthritis, as well as degrading connective tissues such as elastin, collagen, and structured glycoproteins. Certain aspects of vegetable oils provide protection against the degradation of important macromolecules in the body systems. Simply put, they work as anti-agers.

One of the greatest causes of premature aging and tissue degeneration is the presence of free radicals. These super-charged atoms grab anything they find to react. They are a principle cause of cross linking, where fibrous tissue is joined one to another, so reducing the skins elasticity. These molecular fragments are caused during everyday metabolism, but they are mopped up by free radical scavengers – the antioxidants. Free radicals damage cell membranes in the skin and in the body. It's as if the membranes go rancid, go off. That's exactly what happens inside us if free radicals get the upper hand; we go off.

If a cell wall or membrane breaks down, leaks occur. Mixes of compounds that are not meant to mix lead to all manner of troubles and extensive damage can follow. Allergic reactions certainly come into this area. Things that produce free radicals are heated oils (consider oil processing) including frying, and cigarette smoking – every puff contains really big numbers. Here is a good reason to make sure your therapist does not use rancid oil to save money. Rancid oil is a free radical bomb. Look out for, and use, oils rich in vitamin E and the carotenoids, antioxidants, and anti-agers.

Another feature of skin recently discovered are the Langerhans cells. These appear to be intelligent cells that are right up there at the interface with the world. These cells act as part of the immune system and seem to organise wound healing. The concept of a communicant cell is not new. White blood cells call for aid when being overwhelmed by disease bodies. The mechanistic and totally cold analytical approach does not allow for intelligent cellular communication, but has to explain it that way. Likewise with the Langerhans cells, which have been described as 'skin watchers' or overseers. Who knows how they interpret beneficial oils when applied topically.

Vegetable oils, the liquid golden energy of the sun, are simply good for us – in the right form and in the right place.

# 6

# *The Vegetable Oils*

$E$ach oil is unique in itself. Each oil has its own origins and benefits. They are more than carriers. They can be used alone or in combination, singly or blended, or used as solvents for natural extractions. They are as much part of Nature's gift as essential oils.

Providing you use the best grade for the intended purpose, they are safe and reliable. They have been used for thousands of years in body work, baby massage, and beauty massage. Vegetable oils have been part of nutrition and the loving and caring touch for all time. Learn to use them by experience, feel and touch.

Always choose the best quality for the purpose in mind. This means that you should understand what you are buying, especially as a therapist. If one oil is more expensive than another of the same name by more than a few pennies or cents, then there is usually a difference in quality. Do not assume that all refining is bad or that all whole oils are perfect; use the right material for the work at hand. Do not assume that refined oils have exactly the same qualities as their crude counterparts; they do not.

Abbreviations used in the following monographs:

**St**   saturated
**Mo** monounsaturated
**Pu**  polyunsaturated

The percentages supplied are averages or ranges. You will therefore notice that some of the sums do not add up to 100% or exceed it. Trace components are not always noted, and some figures are rounded up or down. The figures are therefore indicative only and for guidance purposes.

Latin names given are a mixture of official EU INCI (INTERNATIONAL NOMENCLATURE COSMETIC INGREDIENTS) names and botanical names. Neem, for example, is given the botanic name rather than the INCI name. The choice taken has been based upon common usage which in its turn is based upon botanical terminology rather than the newer INCI names.

# Name: ALMOND OIL
## Botanic Name: *Prunus amygdalis var.Dulcis (sweet)*

## General Information

The common almond tree comes from Central Asia and spread through Southern Europe between the 8th and the 14th century. It is now cultivated in all Mediterranean countries, around the coasts of the Black Sea, and in California. The tree grows from 6 to 12 metres high and has pink or white flowers. The tree has two forms: the Sweet Almond, used commercially for its oil; and the Bitter Almond (P.amygdalis amara). The flowers of the latter are larger than the cultivated sweet varieties. The fruit is pale green, slightly sueded, and contains the seed – the almond – from which the oil is extracted. Legend tells us that Demophon, the son of Theseus, followed in his father's footsteps by abandoning his love, Phyllis. She committed suicide and became the almond tree. Demophon eventually returned, full of remorse, and hugged the tree. The tree instantly blossomed! A moral for all tree huggers?

## Properties and Uses

Bitter almonds have sometimes been made into a paste used in place of soap for eczema or dermatitis on the hands. The paste is also said to be good for toning down freckles, and makes an efficient deodorant. An essential oil can be produced but the process forms hydro cyanic acid, very toxic. A free-of-acid form exists and is used as flavouring.

The sweet almond is our main concern. Sweet almond paste is mainly used in food recipes such as marzipan, halva, baklava, and cakes. Almond nuts are commonly eaten, and sugar-coated almonds are popular sweets.

Sweet Almond Oil can be rich in essential fatty acid and is used as a popular ingredient for cosmetics such as moisturising and emollient hand creams, body milks, restructuring night creams, and softening massage oils. It is almost an industry standard in Aromatherapy for massage and body work, being widely used and appreciated for its excellent handling characteristics. It is not rapidly absorbed so providing slippage for some length of time. No Aromatherapist should be without it.

Quality and price is highly variable. The oil, when crude, is usually pale yellow with a slight odour. Processing can change this to the ubiquitous, clear, refined versions, which have been robbed of their value the cheap standard of the jobbing beauty salon.

The unsaponifiable content at around 1.5% includes beta-sitosterol, alpha-tocopherol and squalene. In practice I have found good quality oil to handle a little more 'thickly' than expected. As it does not diffuse very quickly it is economic to use for massage that takes time. It has proved useful for dry skin and is quite soothing.

Sweet almond Oil is regarded as monounsaturated and is promoted by Californian producers as a cholesterol-lowering product, so preventing heart disease. Not unnaturally, they claim better results with dietary intake compared to the European Olive Oil. Olive Oil is cheaper, so my advice is to use Olive Oil and eat the nuts or sprinkle them in cooking.

**Typical Fatty Acid Profile**

| C16:0 | st | Palmitic acid | 6 - 8% |
|-------|-----|--------------|--------|
| C18:0 | st | Stearic acid | 0.5 - 2% |
| C18:1 | mo | Oleic acid | 64 - 82% |
| C18:2 | pu | Linoleic acid | 8 - 28% |

Name: ANDIROBA OIL
Botanic Name: *Carapa guianensis*

## General Information

Andiroba is a tall tree and is common in the forests of Guyana, Brazil, and Colombia. It produces fragrant flowers, and fruit that look like large chestnuts, each containing a kernel rich in lipids. Andiroba is a hard, insect resistant wood, and has long been used for timber and for furniture making. Only the kernels and/or the bark is used in traditional medicine. Andiroba is very popular amongst Amazonian tribes, and also in Creole medicine is used in a number of remedies against skin diseases and in medicines for children.

The Wayapi tribe de-husk the nuts by steeping and then exposing the kernels, contained in a palm trunk, to the heat of the sun. The oil simply flows. Undoubtedly the oil has traditional preservative values as head hunting tribes placed their trophies in the oil as part of the mummification process.

## Properties and Uses

Andiroba is very often used as a protector against rain and cold, as well as being a powerful insect repellent. It also has an anti-inflammatory and calming effect on localised itches. In the traditional Amerindian pharmacopoeia, Andiroba is also used as a liniment against muscular fatigue and strain, especially by people active in sports and martial arts.

Andiroba can also be used in any cosmetic product as an active principle or as a carrier in the oily phase, without any proportion limit. It can be used in all skin care products including body lotions, skin restructuring emulsions, anti-wrinkle products, and particularly in creams for dry, dehydrated or damaged skins. ;. Andiroba is best described as a heavy, rich oil with good slippage and characteristics similar to olive, but with more depth. The colour is a light orange with a typical oil odour containing a hint of bitterness.

**Typical Fatty Acid Profile**

| | | | |
|---|---|---|---|
| C16:0 | st | Palmitic acid | 28% |
| C16:1 | mo | Palmitoleic acid | 1% |
| C18:0 | st | Stearic acid | 8.1% |
| C!8:1 | mo | Oleic acid | 50.5% |
| C18:2 | pu | Linoleic acid | 9% |
| C18:3 | pu | alpha Linolenic acid | 0.3% |
| C20:0 | st | Arachidic acid | 1.2% |

Andiroba Oil contains about 5% of unsaponifiable materials.

# Name: APRICOT KERNEL OIL
Botanic Name: *Prunus armeniaca*

## General Information

The Apricot tree is a small fruit tree that grows wild in its native Iran and Manchuria. It was brought to Europe by the Greeks, and has been extensively cultivated since Roman times. Since its introduction to the US in the early 18th century it has become a universally recognised 'fruit'. The fruit is small and fleshy with a lot of fibre, and is now quite common all over the world due to its tasty juice and pulp. Studies on dried Apricots in the diet of Hunza people in the Himalayas gave birth to many dietary ideas.

Whilst there is over production of the fruit in Europe, the oil is not so common. Pure Apricot Oil should not be confused with a mixture of Prunus oils derived from various waste 'stones', hard seeds like cherry pips. Such derived oil should be labelled 'Persic'. Unfortunately, as Apricot Kernel Oil is relatively expensive to produce and apparently chemically little different to Almond Oil, adulteration or confusion is quite common.

Apricots have many feminine associations. The Byzantine Empress of the East, Eudoxia, was pelted with ripe apricots symbolic of her luxurious and exotic life. Many love potions and spells have been woven with the aid of apricots, said to be fruits that arouse passion!

## Properties and Uses

The kernel or nut, sometimes called an 'almond', can be eaten when it is from the cultivated sweet varieties; but the species itself, like the true almond, is bitter and contains a substance producing a hydro cyanic acid which is a dangerous poison. Apricot Kernel Oil contains more polyunsaturated acids for edible purposes than most other commercially available oils. It also has a linoleic acid content and is readily absorbed by the skin, providing tissues with those essential elements as well as high levels of vitamin A precursor.

Apricot Kernel Oil is used in the conditions of atherosclerosis and in external use as an antirheumatic. Practice has indicated a good combination with Cashew Nut Oil and Devils Claw herbal oil wherever painful joints are manifest. In skin care it is valuable as a facial oil due to its light texture, and is typically suited to dry and sensitive skins.

As it has quite a strong odour, the odourless refined material is most common in creams and milks. The colour is light to darker yellow. I find the oil light to use and especially beneficial in skin care or for facial massage work, less so for body work. It seems to be readily absorbed and easy to work with. It blends well, giving a light textural change to other richer oils.

### Typical Fatty Acid Profile

| C16:0 | st | Palmitic acid | 3.6 - 6.6% |
|-------|-----|--------------------|------------|
| C16:1 | mo | Palmitoleic acid | 0.5 - 1.0% |
| C18:0 | st | Stearic acid | 0.5 - 1.5% |
| C18:1 | mo | Oleic acid | 58 - 74% |
| C18:2 | pu | Linoleic acid | 25 – 30% |
| C18:3 | pu | alpha Linolenic acid | 0.3% |

An unsaponifiable content range is between 0.5 - 0.7%

# Name: ARGAN OIL
## Botanic Name: *Argana spinosa*

### General Information

The Argan tree is small and spiky. It grows mostly in the south of Morocco, and is hardly known elsewhere. It bears a fruit that yields an edible nut. The fleshy drupe is also oily. The fruit takes a year to mature, turning  yellow from bright lime green. Photos of Morocco often show pictures of goats feeding whilst climbing trees. This typical scene shows the Argan tree as goats are very partial to the fruit and twigs.

In local tradition the almonds are only milled by hand once the almond has passed through the goats gut! Traditional processing includes roasting the nuts to obtain the flavour and make the oil flow as the mixture is ground and crushed. The mixture is then dowsed in water and the oil floats off. Unsurprisingly, the oil can be a brown, burnt-tasting mixture. Decanting and settling removes the debris and clarifies the oil, which has a distinctive nutty flavour. It takes ten man-hours to work this way for one litre of oil. Most Argan Oil is a product of modern cold press production and refining.

### Properties and Uses

Argan has good resistance to oxidation and is a free radical scavenger. It has much more vitamin E than, say, olive, and of the right type – alpha tocopherol. The oil contains both carotenes and phytosterols.

Argan Oil has good skin softening qualities and is suitable for damaged and mature skin. The oil demonstrates the possibility for good restructuring activity as it is high in unsaturated fatty acids. The seeds yield an unsaturated oil rich in oleic and linoleic acid (as much as 35%). It is best identified for use in cosmetic creams and milks, especially of the richer type, or for its nutritive qualities around the delicate eye area. In practice, I have found it an indifferent massage oil except on skin that shows signs of premature ageing, sun damage, and the more mature skin prone to wrinkles. Use it where there is skin damage. It associates well with Rose Hip Seed Oil used for anti scarring and to avoid stretch marks. The colour is usually mid yellow as crude, and unlikely to come from traditional processing!

**Typical Fatty Acid Profile**

| C16:0 | st | Palmitic acid | 12.6% |
|-------|-----|------------------|-------|
| C16:1 | mo | Palmitoleic acid | 0.1% |
| C18:0 | st | Stearic acid | 5.4% |
| C18:1 | mo | Oleic acid | 48.4% |
| C20:0 | st | Arachidic acid | 0.2% |
| C20:1 | mo | Eicosenoic acid | 0.3% |

The unsaponifiable content usually amounts to 0.8%. Specialised sterols are present, predominantly spinasterol.

# Name: AVELLANA or GEVUINA OIL
Botanic Name: *Gevuina avellana*

**General Information**

The tree owes its name to its close visual resemblance to the common European hazel. There the resemblance ends. They are quite different botanically. Avellana's natural habitat is at the southern end of South America, spanning Chile and Argentina. The name Gevuina comes from the tribal language of the Mapuche Indians who have used the tree for many medicinal and other purposes as well as the seed for food and flour.

This is a tall tree, up to twelve metres high, with tough, dark green leathery leaves. The white flowers give a fruit that changes from green through red to a purple black husk. A true oil bearing nut, the yield is about 50% of oil. Production is usually by cold press, followed by filtration to clarify the oil. The colour is yellow to orange, and the consistency similar to Sweet Almond.

## Properties and Uses

This is an easy oil to work with in massage: it penetrates well but leaves a protective film. It is a monounsaturate and has good keeping qualities. In some parts of the world, animal oils are still used, e.g. Mink Oil. Avellana has similar characteristics to such oils and can replace them. Sensibly Avellana could be used in pet grooming products or treatments. It would also be an ideal component of a heavy duty or protective face or barrier cream, perhaps combining with a balm base to make an unguent style blend. The high content of palmitoleic acid in Avellana should be remembered for all post-menopausal skin; and this oil makes a pleasant, effective moisturising and antiageing blend with Macadamia.

A molecule has been isolated that is similar to some anti-cancer drugs based upon yew tree derivatives. The presence of this molecule suggests that Avellana can be added to any blend being used in cancer care. As with other monounsaturates, the oil would benefit those concerned about their cholesterol levels.

### Typical Fatty Acid Profile

| | | | |
|---|---|---|---|
| C16:0 | st | Palmitic acid | 1 – 5% |
| C16:1 | mo | Palmitoleic acid | 18 –28% |
| C18:1 | mo | Oleic acid | 32 – 49% |
| C18:2 | pu | Linoleic acid | 7 – 15% |
| C20:0 | st | Arachidic acid | 1 – 3% |
| C20:1 | mo | Gondoic acid | 6 – 14% |
| C22:1 | mo | Erucic acid | 5 – 12% |

Unsaponifiable content lies between 0.2% and 0.9%.

# Name: AVOCADO OIL
Botanic Name: *Persea americana Miller*

## General Information

An Avocado pear tree can reach 15 metres but in cultivation is usually a lot less. The tree is pleasing to look at, with a greyish bark and shiny dark green foliage. It's a native of swamplands, locally called 'alligator pear'. The fruit – the rich, savoury tasting Avocado Pear – is considered to be of great nutritional food value and readily digestible. The pears come in a variety of green to purple shades. Avocado is not a pear at all, just pear shaped, and in botany it belongs to the Laurel family.

Avocado originated in the Americas, hence the second part of its Latin name, americana. The alternative Latin name (and official INCI name, do the Europeans resent the Americans so much!) P.gratissima means 'pleasant' and describes the fruit. It was very well known by the Aztecs and native peoples of Central America who used it for their ailments, and also to protect their skins from the parching, hot, dry winds of that area. Several parts of the tree are used in native medicine. Legend states that it is also used on hair to promote its growth. Its most famous use is in the Mexican guacamole dish, the ingredients being Avocado pulp, coriander leaf, capsicum, and tomato.

Oil is obtained from the oily flesh. Desiccated Avocado yields its oil to pressure and centrifuge extraction; solvent extraction is not usual. An oil is obtainable from the seed or stone but is not commonly found. Though said to have anti-tumour properties, the stone oil is regarded as toxic. Similar problems surround Apricot Oil and its derivatives. The *fresh* pulp oil is a bright green, due to its chlorophyll content, but this very quickly degrades in sunlight to brown. Be aware of this when buying green Avocado Oil. Sometimes a green colouring agent is added to refined oil to make it look more natural! If it's green and does not go brown, beware! Oil on the turn, poor colour, should never be used. The oil composition varies tremendously depending upon the variety.

The Conquistadors of Spain brought the fruit to Europe. The Spaniards could not get their tongue around the native sound of 'ahuaguatl' and so the name 'avocado' came into parlance. I have seen it grown from South Africa to Israel. It is a world crop.

## Properties and Uses

The flesh of the fruit yields a green oil, degrading quickly to brown with a spicy odour. Avocado Oil is traditionally used for softening and protective properties for the skin. It promotes cell regeneration and has a well-known action on dry, fragile, and distended skins with tendencies to damage from sunburn. It is an oil that is worth including in all sun care products, and could combine well with sesame. Repeated massage applications reveal an increase in hydration of the upper layers of the skin, and an improvement in the skin's elastic properties. It has a high sterol content, 10%, and is used as an adjunctive therapy for arthritic pain. It has a unique feature in containing vitamin D, even more than eggs. It would be beneficial to include the oil in all preparations for dark skinned people living in low sunshine conditions. Its traditional use suggests that it is worth combining it with Rosemary essential oil to produce a hair stimulant.

In practice I have found it not so diffusive as its reputation suggests. Some semi-refined materials, discoloured and deodorised, can be sought out, a halfway house from total denaturing. The refined oil of industry is a pale yellow. Avocado in general does permeate quite deeply making it a good carrier for essential oils. I like to combine it with a lighter oil for whole body massage work. In the right combination, due to its lecithin and squalene content, a very smooth touch can be obtained.

The sterol content suggests that it might well be beneficial for women with post-menopausal skin prone to premature ageing. Combined with Macadamia Oil, such a blend would not only be emollient but also have restructuring potential.

**Typical Fatty Acid Profile**

| | | | |
|---|---|---|---|
| C16:0 | st | Palmitic acid | 7 - 32% |
| C16:1 | mo | Palmitoleic acid | 2 - 13% |
| C18:0 | st | Stearic acid | 0.5 - 1.5% |
| C18:1 | mo | Oleic acid | 36 - 80% |
| C18:2 | pu | Linoleic acid | 6 - 18% |
| C18:3 | pu | alpha Linolenic acid | 0 - 5% |

The unsaponifiable content is high 2 – 11% and is mainly of sitosterol, campesterol, and avenasterol along with squalene.


# Name: BABASSU OIL
Botanic Name: *Orbignya oleifera*


## General Information

The Babassu tree looks like the palm tree of people's dreams. It grows to an average of 20 metres, so it's big! Babassu is a coloniser, and after ground clearance is the first tree to be back. It is a native of Brazil and was named by the Tupi tribe. The fruit or drupes come in clusters born by both male and female flowers on the same tree. These clusters look like mini coconuts. Babassu Oil is generally found only as a refined oil. It is certainly oil bearing – the kernel contains 70% oil by weight. This oil has similar chemical and physical characteristics to Coconut Oil.

## Properties and Uses

The oil is used mainly for cooking, and industrial purposes such as soap and detergent manufacture. The oil is lightest yellow to white, without odour, and semi-solid. It is best used for cosmetics such as lip balms and hair care preparations designed especially for dry, brittle, and damaged hair. This oil is composed almost entirely of triglycerides, with only the barest trace of other components such as mono and di-glycerides, sterols, and lactones. Babassu Oil is used in the Americas quite widely in the cosmetic industry and is recommended for suntan preparations, skin care creams, cleansing milks, and lipsticks.

### Typical Fatty Acid Profile

| | | | |
|---|---|---|---|
| C6:0 | st | Caproic acid | 0.2% |
| C8:0 | st | Caprylic acid | 4% |
| C10:0 | st | Capric acid | 7% |
| C12:0 | st | Lauric acid | 50% |
| C14:0 | st | Myristic acid | 20% |
| C16:0 | st | Palmitic acid | 11% |
| C18:0 | st | Stearic acid | 3.5% |
| C18:1 | mo | Oleic acid | 12.5% |
| C18:2 | pu | Linoleic acid | 1.5% |

## Name: BLACK CUMIN
Botanic Name: *Nigella sativa*

### General Information

Any English country garden boasts the hardy annual 'Love in a Mist' referring to the way the flowers are surrounded by fronds. Other common names include fennel flower, Roman coriander and nutmeg flower. These all speak of the seeds' spice balsamic odour, which is not unpleasant but quite strong. The seeds have been used as a pepper substitute.

Black Cumin Oil cold pressed from the small black tough little seeds has been a favourite in the Middle East and Asia from time immemorial. The oil colour is usually a dark yellow brown. It is mentioned in the Bible and no doubt was_a favourite of the Pharaohs. The main supply comes from Egypt and Syria together with Turkey. It has quite a strong spice odour when cold pressed and unrefined if from Turkey, but the Syrian version is milder. Like poppy seeds and caraway, black cumin is found as a digestive flavouring in breads and even in pastas throughout the Middle East.

## Properties and Uses

Black Cumin can be compared with Evening Primrose and Borage oils. It is a rich source of unsaturated fatty acids. Linoleic acid is the major constituent and can be as high as 60%. This means it makes an excellent food supplement and can be added to salad dressings. It is increasingly found as a capsule supplement. The seeds are used to make an infusion as a digestive.

In Aromatherapy and body work the seeds might be considered as the base of a scrub or exfoliating mixture. The oil could be incorporated in such a product perhaps in a gel base with floral waters. Detoxification can be taken further by blending with either citrus or conifer oils. Black cumin mixes well with Jojoba to provide a fortifying and emollient blend. A little goes a long way and, like Neem, some expert blending work with essential oils needs to be done to turn the odour to a sweet fragrance if using the crude types.

### Typical Fatty Acid Profile

| | | | |
|---|---|---|---|
| C16:0 | st | Palmitic | 12% |
| C18:0 | st | Stearic | 3% |
| C18:1 | mo | Oleic | 23% |
| C18:2 | pu | Linoleic | 56% |
| C18:3 | pu | Linolenic | 0.3% |

# Name: BLACKCURRANT SEED OIL
## Botanic Name: *Ribes nigrum*

### General Information

A typically northern hemisphere cultivated shrub or fruit bush. The small clusters of black, round berries are loaded with vitamin C. The whole bush is aromatic with a typical fresh odour. Everyone knows it partly due to the Nestlé Company who produce a famous cordial drink called Ribena. This Company has cornered the market for this oil. Surprisingly therefore, in history it is virtually unheard of, except as a rarely used medicinal plant, until the mid 1800's. It was drink that led the way – Crème de Cassis, the liqueur of Dijon. In England it was blackcurrant jam. The Latin name is likely derived from old Norse languages.

### Properties and Uses

Blackcurrant Seed Oil is a natural vegetable seed oil famed for its composition in long-chain polyunsaturated fatty acids. It is rich in Gamma Linoleic Acid. The body converts this material into molecules that are vital parts of our immune system and blood coagulation system. Gamma linoleic acid is a direct precursor of prostaglandins and thramboxanes.

For external use, Blackcurrant Seed Oil is a pleasant, mobile oil presenting anti-ageing, moisturising, and restructuring properties. Skin elasticity is vital, and GLA is just as vital in maintaining the structure. Fly away and baby hair can best benefit from an occasional application. With a light yellow colour, I suggest it is best used as an ingredient or supportive oil in blending.

### Typical Fatty Acid Profile

| | | | |
|---|---|---|---|
| C16:0 | st | Palmitic acid | 6% |
| C18:0 | st | Stearic acid | 5% |
| C18:1 | mo | Oleic acid | 11 - 12% |
| C18:2 | pu | Linoleic acid | 47 – 48% |
| C18:3 | pu | gamma Linolenic acid | 16 –17% |

| C18:3 | pu | alpha Linolenic acid | 12 – 13% |
| C18:4 | pu | Octadecatretraenoic acid | 3% |
| C20:1 |    | Eicosenoic acid | 1.1% |

The oil also yields an unsaponifiable content of no more than 4%.

## Name: BORAGE OIL
**Botanic Name: *Borago officinalis***

### General Information

Borage grows abundantly in western Mediterranean areas (such as Spain and North Africa), and it is now cultivated in nearly all European countries, the British Isles, and right across to North America. Bees love the blue star-like flowers, which can also be used to decorate a fresh salad. The flowers have given this ancient herb the new name 'Starflower'. I first came across this when a Boots Company research chemist phoned me to learn if I had heard of such a substance. Of course I said no, only to learn much later that the old herb had been given a new marketing name. The English, lovers of claret, sometimes would add borage leaves to make a 'herb claret' to lift black moods. The common name is derived from Arabic and has the original meaning of 'father of sweat'. The similar Latin name also carries the meaning of 'courage' and was used as a talisman in ancient, dangerous times.

Borage bristles with long rough hairs making it a prickly or rough plant to handle. Its flowers are sky blue and they blossom from May to September. The plant is rich in honey-producing nectar, and the seeds yield about 40% of their weight in lipids.

The fresh plant tastes like a mixture of cucumber and shellfish! The young leaves are eaten in salads, in soup, or as spinach. The Germans still add borage to soups, omelettes and doughnuts! The fresh flowers are edible and can be eaten candied.

## Properties and Uses

Borage is well known for being rich in GLA. It is one of the richest sources known and readily available in capsules. Borage Oil is sometimes used to boost the GLA content of other oils such as evening primrose. Herbalists have long said that borage seeds are good for lactating women. GLA is an important part of human breast milk. The seed oil of borage is used in cosmetics for its soothing and moisturising properties on dry and sensitive skin. It also purifies and tones combination and tired skin, and brightens up grey hair. It is used in anti-ageing and wrinkle preparations to fight dehydration and loss of skin elasticity, and because of its regenerative and firming properties.

Use it to boost the immune system by internal consumption. Folk after retirement age can benefit greatly from a daily intake of GLA. It is ideal as an additive to any number of skin preparations, and gives a rich body to nutritive and night-time creams.

### Typical Fatty Acid Profile

| | | | |
|---|---|---|---|
| C18:2 | pu | Linoleic acid | 30 - 40% |
| C18:3 | pu | gamma Linolenic acid | 8 - 25% |
| C18:1 | mo | Oleic acid | 15 - 20% |
| C16:0 | st | Palmitic acid | 9 - 12% |
| C18:0 | st | Stearic acid | 3 - 4% |
| C20:1 | mo | Eicosenoic acid | 2 – 6% |

The total of unsaponifiable components is within the range.

# Name: CAMELLIA OIL
Botanic Name: *Camellia japonica*

## General Information

There is a Fragrant Earth Company in Japan, and there seems a special affinity between that Company's biophilic philosophy and the Japanese love of simplistic art and form. Camellia grows particularly well in Eastern Japan where the winters are especially cold and dry. The Japanese characters for camellia symbolise the meaning 'Tree of Spring'. As in the south-west of England, the bushes can grow to 8 meters and beyond. The bush, in different varieties, blossoms all winter long (even under snow in January and February), after which the flowers are replaced by nuts which are then picked for their oil in the autumn. Tea is a camellia.

Camellia Oil has been used for many hundreds of years by the Japanese people for the care of their hair, scalp, and skin. In the Kyoto area, women used Camellia Oil to enhance their long, black hair. The women living in the Oshima Island near Izu, where Camellias grow everywhere, are famous for their marvellous hair. Although exotic sounding, it is a good food oil, being used for salad dressing and as the right oil for Tempura dishes.

The best Camellia Oil still comes from the Oshima area. Do not confuse this with 'Camelina', which comes from the cabbage family.

## Properties and Uses

For many years it has been recognised that this natural product is perfectly safe to use and can be added to any cosmetic product as an active principle, or as a noble carrier oil, without any particular limits. It is commonly used as a lubricant in surgery and as an excipient for the direct injection of vitamins into the body. The virgin form has a soft yellow colour and a not unpleasant light oil odour. It is a very safe oil to use with little likelihood of any reactions.

As an oil for toiletries and cosmetics, Camellia Oil has excellent skin and hair conditioning properties. It has skin restructuring and moisturising properties, and makes a superb nail strengthener. Because of these properties, it is a good active ingredient in shampoo bases, after-sun products, eye gels, hand creams, nail products, and skin creams for mature, damaged, and dry skin.

I find it one of my favourite oils to use in massage. It has light body but not the 'stickiness' of Olive Oil. On the expensive side neat, it blends well with Walnut (another favourite) and Sweet Almond. This results in a very mobile, readily absorbed oil that provides good slippage without greasiness. Camellia should be used by any Aromatherapist specialising in facial treatments and anti-scarring treatments.

### Typical Fatty Acid Profile

| C18:1 | mo | Oleic acid | 80% |
|-------|-----|---------------|------|
| C18:2 | pu | Linoleic acid | 9% |
| C16:0 | st | Palmitic acid | 9% |
| C18:0 | st | Stearic acid | 1% |
| C20:0 | st | Arachidic acid | 1% |

## Name: CANOLA & RAPESEED OIL
### Botanic Name: *Brassica napus*

### General Information

Rapeseed is the common name in Europe. Canola is a variety of Rapeseed that has been bred to reduce intolerance and toxicity problems in winter cattle feed. Canola is an annual plant, the stem of which can be more than three feet high. It bears blue-green leaves, and the large flowers are cross-shaped and golden yellow in colour and appear in close clusters before flowering time. The fruit contains small, delicately spotted seeds. Rapeseed may either come from Africa or southern Europe. It is grown in vast quantities across China. In more recent times, fields of bright yellow have become a common sight in England along with its musty smell and irritating pollen. It has been well known in Russia and China for many years. Since the early 1980's, the Canola variety has been mainly cultivated in Canada where it has almost replaced normal rapeseed. The very name is derived from 'Can(ada)' and 'Oleum' the Latin for oil. Watch out for Genetically Modified crops.

These are highly industrialised crops. The oil has a completely bland taste and flavour. This makes it ideal for some areas of the industrial food process industries. The waste is great for cattle feed.

## Properties and Uses

Canola is mostly unsaturated oil and would be capable of lowering choles-terol levels in the blood, according to Manitoba University reports. In theory it should be good at regulating epidermal skin behaviour. It favourably replaces the normal Rapeseed Oil in different markets. Rapeseed contains a toxic substance called 'erucic acid'. Rapeseed can contain nearly 50% of this acid, implicated by some studies in heart disease and possibly cancers. I have seen organically grown rapeseed in Scandinavia, but still its profile suggests it should be left alone. Canola, because it is bland and cheap, has been seized upon by the typical US small-time cosmetic companies, who push it hard to Aromatherapists. It still has to be highly processed to yield oil, and does not come from a simple, naturally oil-bearing source. With Linoleic acid and Linolenic acid present at nearly 35%, and bearing in mind the closeness of these substances to the intercellular cement, canola's use is hardly surprising where hype replaces more noble materials. Surely there are better materials than those engineered for the great Canadian plains and agribusiness. Canola is used for low cost body hygiene products; hand creams; skin care products for the face, particularly for areas around the eyes; and mature and dry skins.

### Typical Fatty Acid Profile; Canola

| | | | |
|---|---|---|---|
| C16:0 | st | Palmitic acid | 4.5% |
| C18:0 | st | Stearic acid | 4.5% |
| C18:1 | mo | Oleic acid | 59% |
| C18:2 | pu | Linoleic acid | 21% |

| C18:3 | pu | Linolenic acid | 11% |
| C22:0 | st | Behenic acid | 4.5% |
| C22:1 | mo | Erucic acid | 4.5% |

Unsaponifiables, including tocopherol, range between 0.7 – 2%.

# Name: CARROT OIL (OLEORESIN)
## Botanic Name: *Daucus carota*

### General Information

Carrot Oil is one of the most confusing substances around. Many different things are sold as Carrot Oil. Beware of the cheap and cheerful! The carrot's claim to fame is its vitamin A content. However, the herbal oil is based on the wild carrot, common name Queen Anne's Lace, which has a small white root and no resemblance to the cultivated red root carrot. The latter also yields a lovely fragrant essential oil from the seed, which has a low oil content, below 12%.

Fresh, edible carrot root is nearly all water (85%), but it is rich in carotenes hence its colour. The carotene content of carrot is mainly beta-carotene. The root contains miniscule amounts of lipids, so crushing a carrot does not give an oil despite what you may read in lightweight health and beauty articles. However, fresh carrot pulp is very healing, analgesic, and stops bleeding. Rather than pressing, the carrot has to be either macerated in another oil, usually Sunflower Oil; or the carotenes are extracted by solvent, yielding the oleoresin, which is then diluted, to make it workable, into Corn Oil. As you can imagine, various grades exist and over the counter products may be little more than tainted and coloured carrier oil. The best quality specifies a 0.2% concentration of beta-carotenes.

## Properties and Uses

Those old enough to remember the Second World War may recall the need to eat more carrots, based on the exploits of the night fighter pilot Cats Eyes Cunningham. Carrots improve vision, especially night vision, hence his success. The principle use is as an additive to a blend or product to introduce the carotenes as precursors to vitamin A. The oil is intensely orange yellow and can colour the skin or cream leading to staining of clothes, etc. Vitamin A deficiency leads to dry skin and sebaceous glands atrophy. Carotenes are also strong free radical blockers; hence the oil's use in so many anti-ageing preparations. It is a useful addition to sun creams and after-sun lotions.

Certainly the Aromatherapists friend and ally, this oil can be utilised in many ways but not as a massage oil unless it is an extract or herbal oil made from the wild carrot.

### Typical Fatty Acid Profile:
Inapplicable

## Name: CASHEW NUT OIL
Botanic Name: *Anacardium occidentale*

## General Information

Cashew nuts always make me think of India. The Cashew tree is actually a native of Brazil, and was discovered by the Portuguese and taken to their African and Asian colonies, including India. India is now by far the largest cashew nut producer. The name is derived from a Tupi tribe name 'akaju', turned to the Portuguese 'caju'. The Cashew tree is an evergreen and its branches are covered with dense foliage. It produces fruit after four to five years, though can produce much earlier if well tended. It needs very little water, can grow in poor soils, and colonises quickly.

The cashew fruit has a very unusual appearance. What seems an apple-like fruit, the fleshy part, holds the nut at its base like an appendage. These unusual nuts are kidney-shaped and vary in colour from yellow to red. They are gathered when the fruit is ripe and fall on the ground, then dried for several days. To obtain the kernel, the shell is crushed by hand. The nuts are very rich and a satisfying and wholesome food source of vitamins.

**Properties and Uses**

In Ayurveda, the Indian system of medicine developing for some 3,000 years, the Cashew nut has been in use since the 16th century as a stimulant, a rejuvenator, and an appetiser.

The Cashew fruit is high in vitamin C, and the nut is very rich in vitamins A, D, K, PP, and especially E; calcium; phosphorus; iron; amino acids; and fatty acids. The nuts are roughly 20% protein with a good amino acid balance, 45% fats, and 20% carbohydrates. The nuts are considered to alleviate kidney disorders and are used for arthritis and rheumatism. Collagen and connective tissue disorders can also respond to this multi-role nut.

Cashew Nut Oil is used as a carrier for liniment, as an anaesthetic in leprosy and psoriasis, and for the treatment of blisters, warts, corns and ulcers. Because of its natural richness in vitamin E, this oil has a free radical scavenging activity and has a natural resistance to oxidation. It also makes this a 'must have' addition for Aromatherapists in the treatment of skin ageing problems. This oil has wide uses in cosmetics such as skin care products, hand creams, massage oils, sun products, lip balms, etc.

As a product that is usually obtained by simple expression, I have found it to have a distinctive aroma when used alone. The oil is a good strong orange yellow and will colour creams. The aroma is generally lost in creams and milks, or easily disguised. I have also found that the natural waxes are very temperature sensitive and often these 'white bits' can be seen in the oil, a good sign of naturalness. In northern climes and cold conditions, these waxes can, however, crystallise and make a balm, for instance, feel gritty.

**Typical Fatty Acid Profile**

| | | | |
|---|---|---|---|
| C16:0 | st | Palmitic acid | 10% |
| C18:0 | st | Stearic acid | 9% |
| C18:1 | mo | Oleic acid | 60% |
| C18:2 | pu | Linoleic acid | 20% |
| C18:3 | pu | alpha Linolenic acid | 1% |

# Name: CASTOR OIL
Botanic Name: *Ricinus communis L.*

## General Information
The plant is a quick growing herbaceous sub shrub which can grow up to fifteen feet high when cultivated in temperate zones, but it can also be a tough thorny shrub or tree of about forty-five feet high in much warmer climates. It is generally believed to be native to Africa or India and the major Castor Oil producing countries include Brazil, China and India.

The parts used are the ripe seeds, which are colourless to pale yellow, and the oil can be obtained by cold pressing. The oil is remarkably stable and does not turn rancid easily. The seed, however, is extremely toxic and can cause serious symptoms in certain individuals (such as asthma, skin rashes, eye irritations, etc.) and should not be eaten. However, this toxic substance, known as 'ricin', does not come out in the oil.

Castor Oil, alongside Olive and Moringa, has one of the longest pedigrees of human use. The ancient Egyptians used it as a purgative, and it was known by the Romans as especially useful to rid oneself of skin 'defects'. In North Africa it is the staple ingredient oil in many dubious magic potions.

Castor Oil is extracted in many ways, but traditionally by sun drying the seeds and then pressure to form this relatively thick oil. The beans contain toxic resin that can be activated by too much heat. Numerous grades exist.

## Properties and Uses

Castor Oil has cathartic properties. It is a laxative, acting on the small intestine, and producing purgation 2 to 8 hours after ingestion. There is a long history of medical use in both East and West. Castor Oil does have emollient properties on the skin, and due to its viscosity can be considered where moisture needs to be locked in or out.

Castor Oil is used in food products as a component of protective coatings in tablets and as a flavour component (e.g. butter and nut flavours) in non-alcoholic beverages, frozen dairy desserts, and confectionery. Its many industrial uses include softening materials, treating leather, waterproofing and so on. It is also used in cosmetics as an ingredient in lipsticks, hair products, ointments, creams, lotions, transparent soaps, suppository basis, and others. It finds little value in Aromatherapy, being very thick, viscous. It has a very distinct odour and is usually a pale yellow. When sulphonated or hydrogenated, it does form the base of a common dispersant in water and so occurs carrying essential oils in many natural bath oils, breath fresheners, etc. Hydrogenated forms are used as emulsion stabilisers.

Following Roman advice, my wife has found it effective in treatments when applied to skin blemishes such as brown patches, liver spots, age spots, etc.! Castor Oil packs combined with Lemon drink have been promoted as immune stimulants in the treatment of AIDS sufferers.

### Typical Fatty Acid Profile

| | | | |
|---|---|---|---|
| C16:0 | st | Palmitic acid | 1% |
| C18:0 | st | Stearic acid | 1% |
| C18:1 | mo | Oleic acid | 3% |
| C18:2 | pu | Linoleic acid | 3 - 4% |
| C12-OH 18:1 | mo | Ricinoleic acid | 89 - 90% |

Castor Oil also contains 0.5 to 1% unsaponifiable elements.

# Name: CHAULMOOGRA OIL
## Botanic Name: *Hydnocarpus laurifolia*

## General Information
The name sounds so wonderfully Indian, it just sounds exotic, and it is. The Chaulmoogra tree is common; it grows about 15 to 20 metres high and is native to the tropical forests of India. Its leaves are oblong; its flowers are small, greenish white, solitary or in fascicles. The fruits contain numerous small seeds, the kernel of which consists of about 60% oil. The oil is specific in application to chronic skin conditions.

## Properties and Uses
Chaulmoogra Oil ranges from pale yellow when semi-solid, to dark yellow as it melts. It has a characteristic odour and is soluble in most organic solvents. This oil is a gastro-intestinal irritant and *must not* be taken internally. This oil is mainly used in the treatment of leprosy, wounds, and ulcers. Applied locally, it has properties that help relieve joint discomforts and pain. This oil has also been used in South India in cases of chronic skin and eye infections. It is recommended for rheumatism, sprains, bruises, sciatica, and chest infections, and is used in dressings for wounds and ulcers due to certain antiseptic properties.

In Aromatherapy, Chaulmoogra Oil can be used in products for skin irritations due to intense cold and dry environmental conditions, i.e. face and neck care products, and cream for chapped hands and feet. It is one of those 'additional' oils that can contribute to a fine blend. It could sensibly combine with German chamomile and Devils claw in a gel against inflammatory pain. It would sensibly form the oil base of a rich cream for damaged, rough hands.

### Typical Fatty Acid Profile

| | | | |
|---|---|---|---|
| C16:0 | st | Palmitic acid | 4% |
| C18:1 | st | Oleic acid | 6% |
| 13-Cp13:1 | mo | Gorlic acid | 12% |

| 13-Cp13:0 st | Chaulmoogric acid | 27% |
| 11-Cp11:0 st | Hydnocarpic acid | 49% |

## Name: COCONUT OIL
**Botanic Name:** *Cocos nucifera*

### General Information

Originally from the islands of the Indian Ocean, coconut is palm tree 20 to 30 metres high, and is widely cultivated in Indonesia, Malaysia, and the West Indies. It was introduced into Brazil, Mexico, and Africa. It grows well in hot, humid climates at low-altitudes and by the seaside. It's the tree we see in all the tropical Island pictures of idyllic beach scenes. This tall tree bears palmate leaves that can reach from 6 to 8 metres long. The fruit is a large ovoid nut that weighs several kilos. Its shell is thick and fibrous, and the white flesh inside the seed, when dry, yields Coprah Oil. The central cavity inside the seed is full of opalescent liquid, known as 'coconut water' or 'coconut milk', which is a delicious and bacteria-free sterile drink. The nut is used to flavour desserts and sweets, and coconut milk is the staple for many oriental sauces.

The name is said to derive from the Portuguese word 'coquo' meaning a 'goat kid'. With a bit of imagination, seen end on, there can be the appearance of two eyes and a tiny mouth. The Portuguese, we sometimes forget, were modern Europe's first big time explorers.

The oil or butter should be viewed mainly as a highly industrialised material. There are many forms and qualities. For example, there is a Virgin form, and a Hydrogenated form with a higher melt point. The Virgin is usually solid and white, or clear with a slight yellow tone. Toiletries often disguise chemical sounding names like 'lauryl sulphate' behind phrases such as 'natural coconut derived wash active substances'. Coconut Oil is the starting material for a number of detergent processes.

## Properties and Uses

Being a mainly saturated fat, it is stable and storage is relatively easy. Coconut Oil has skin softening, moisturising, and film-forming properties. Although called an oil, it is mostly a soft butter. It depends upon the temperature, melting at 25° C. It is used in the making of 'Monoi', and in certain countries the pulp is used as a balm to stimulate hair growth. It is used in sun products and foam baths, and is added to products for dry and damaged hair because of its good coating properties. It is also recommended in moisturising body oils for the treatment of dry skin and for calming sensitive and delicate skins, and in lip balms.

Roofs, mats, and clothing items are made with coconut leaves; and the fibres from the shell, coir, are used in the making of doormats, brushes, ropes, and hats. The fibre also crops up in the garden as mulching material.

Coconut Oil, if not incorporated as a thickener in cream and other bases, is best used on its own by the discerning therapist. It gives good slippage in massage and remains on the skin surface for some time. The skin is left smooth and in svelte condition. It is economic to use and holds essential oils very well. Many treatments can be devised allowing this oil to melt onto the body, and indeed into the hair as tonic for dry or devitalised hair.

Do not confuse this natural butter oil with 'Fractionated', 'Thin' or 'Light' Coconut oil which is a highly refined and processed material lacking the substance of the real material. Promoted only for its cheapness in Aromatherapy, and popularised in the US, it lacks all the C:8-C:12 components.

### Typical Fatty Acid Profile

| | | | |
|---|---|---|---|
| C8:0 | st | Caprylic acid | 6 - 10% |
| C10:0 | st | Capric acid | 5 - 10% |
| C12:0 | st | Lauric acid | 39 - 54% |
| C14:0 | st | Myristic acid | 15 - 23% |
| C16:0 | st | Palmitic acid | 6 - 11% |
| C18:0 | st | Stearic acid | 1 - 4% |
| C18:1 | mo | Oleic acid | 4 - 11% |
| C18:2 | pu | Linoleic acid | 1 - 2% |

Unsaponifiables are present at a rate of between 0.6 - 1.5%.

# Name: COPRAH OIL
## Botanic Name: *Cocos nucifera*

### General Information

Coprah Oil is extracted from the white albumen of the coconut. Coprah seems to be the trade of all the romantic literature of South Sea schooners. It is no more than the dried or desiccated flesh of the coconut and the main starting material for Coconut Oil.

Polynesia has a rich tradition of using Coconut Oil in a variety of ways. It is the basic massage oil, slightly warmed for the traditional Huna style massage. The women of the area are renowned for their thick, black, glossy hair. This is attributed to the tradition of combing Coprah or Coconut Oil through the hair. In the West, the oil is applied to the hair and left in for 15 - 30 minutes before washing out. Use the least aggressive shampoo you can afford. Coprah Oil is also used in sun care, but remember it has no natural sunscreens; it is only in effect a good, thick moisturiser so should be applied very regularly. It does, however, form the basis of many commercial preparations with added sunscreens.

### Properties and Uses

Coprah Oil has the same properties and virtues as Coconut Oil and is used for the same purposes.

#### Typical Fatty Acid Profile

It has the same profile as coconut being the same thing.

| | | | |
|---|---|---|---|
| C8:0 | st | Caprylic acid | 6 - 10% |
| C10:0 | st | Capric acid | 5 - 10% |
| C12:0 | st | Lauric acid | 39 - 54% |
| C14:0 | st | Myristic acid | 15 - 23% |
| C16:0 | st | Palmitic acid | 6 - 11% |

| C18:0 | st | Stearic acid | 1 - 4% |
| C18:1 | mo | Oleic acid | 4 - 11% |
| C18:2 | pu | Linoleic acid | 1 - 2% |

Unsaponifiables are present at a rate of between 0.6 - 1.5%.

Name: CORN OIL

Botanic Name: *Zea Mays*

## General Information

Corn Oil originates from what people in the UK call 'maize'. It was essentially a by-product of the cereal that grows throughout Europe and America. Now it is huge business following the change in frying habits that demanded vegetable oils. Corn is subject to much Genetic Modification and can be thought to be mostly contaminated if bought from the US without guarantees.

Corn, or maize, originated in Central America and was the staple of many Native American tribes. All plants have been cultivated and no wild ancestor has ever been found. Maize is a living tribute to our earliest agricultural ancestors. Motifs crop up in wall paintings and pottery from ancient times. The Mayans believed mankind was made from corn flour. The Incas used corn as funerary gifts. Early Mexican tribes saw maize as representative of a Goddess, the corn and star maiden. The different colours of the seed, mostly golden yellow but varying from brown to red to almost purple, seem to have fascinated our early ancestors, and the Blue corn became especially sacred. The Hopi tribe and others maintain this even today. Even in the North the Iroquois prayed for corn and its sisters. This spiritual overtone should also be taken into consideration with the arguments for and against GM crops.

## Properties and Uses

Corn Oil is usually highly refined for the food industry. Everything from breakfast cereal to biscuits, margarine, and chocolate uses this oil. In cosmetics, it is used as an emollient and even a conditioner in toothpaste. Of course, it is plentiful, and cheap, and refined, and fractionated to provide by-products like vitamin E. So there is no guarantee vitamin E is present unless guaranteed in the specification. Do not rely on phrases such as 'Corn Oil contains...'. What you need is *this* Corn Oil contains...'!

The oil is derived from the germ of the seed. Corn Oil is very rich in linoleic acid and can be used in health food products. It is generally used in cooking for frying and baking. Due to its highly processed nature, it does not generally find favour with Aromatherapists. Nevertheless, Aromatherapists do use Wheatgerm Oil, which undergoes similar processing and refining. One of the characteristics of the best quality Corn Oil is its superior content in unsaturated fats. Its keeping quality is enhanced by relatively large volumes of vitamin E with its antioxidant, free radical scavenging properties.

The standard for a good Wheatgerm Oil content of Vitamin E is 0.2% whereas Corn Oil comes in at 0.6%, provided that it is not refined out. It can be a valuable oil in the right circumstances, and especially useful in creams and blends to add to shelf life.

### Typical Fatty Acid Profile

| | | | |
|---|---|---|---|
| C14:0 | st | Myristic acid | 0.1% |
| C16:0 | st | Palmitic acid | 8 - 13% |
| C16:1 | mo | Palmitoleic acid | 1% |
| C18:0 | st | Stearic acid | 1 - 4% |
| C18:1 | mo | Oleic acid | 24 - 32% |
| C18:2 | pu | Linoleic acid | 55 - 62% |
| C18:3 | pu | alpha Linolenic acid | 2% |
| C20:0 | st | Arachidic cid | 1% |

The unsaponifiable content, particularly rich in sterols and tocopherols, can be up to 2%.

# Name: COTTONSEED OIL
## Botanic Name: *Gossypium hirsutum*


## General Information

This is another example of a highly refined and industrialised oil. It is not one of the groups of nuts and seeds we can call naturally 'oil bearing'. It is used for economy. Cotton is probably easy to visualise with its seed heads of fluffy white bolls. There are varieties that do not have the fluffy bolls- the so-called black cotton mainly used for oil production. 'Hirsutum' means 'hairy' and refers directly to the seed head. The plant is found in many countries, but the big producers of the fibres are Egypt, Russia, China, India, and, of course, the USA. Its probably been worked for at least 5,000 years.

The seeds contain a toxic substance called 'gossypol' which has to be eliminated if an edible oil is required. The possible yield is quite low so extreme pressure and heat is required to produce a usable oil, which is thick and unpleasantly tarry before refining. At the height of the Industrial Revolution in the UK, when cotton spinning was a major industry, Cottonseed Oil accounted for a large proportion of UK vegetable oil use.


## Properties and Uses

Cotton is universally used the world over for everything from clothing to tyre walls. Cotton, or its oil, finds its way into many unexpected things such as paint, varnish, explosives, cotton imitations, and man made fibres. You will not find a Cottonseed Oil that is not at least bleached, deodorised, and fully refined. The normal colour is a mid yellow. It makes its way into cheap natural cosmetics and soaps, where its fluffy origins can be smoothed into adventurous copy writing. It crops up in many cheap creams, baby products, and nail products.

Sometimes it is used in massage for slippage but not by Aromatherapists with an eye to better products or who are working in health care. Play is made of its essential fatty acid content and softening qualities, but never take it internally. Allergy to the oil is also reported. Its prime use is economy of product with a so-called 'natural' claim. It is used to adulterate more expensive oils.

### Typical Fatty Acid Profile

| | | | |
|---|---|---|---|
| C16:0 | st | Palmitic acid | 23 - 28% |
| C18:0 | st | Stearic acid | 2 - 3% |
| C18:1 | mo | Oleic acid | 14 - 21% |
| C18:2 | pu | Linoleic acid | 45 - 57% |

## Name: EVENING PRIMROSE OIL
Botanic Name: *Oenothera biennis*

### General Information

A native to North America, the Evening Primrose has always been noted for its medicinal properties, but it was only some four decades ago that researchers confirmed that the plant was indeed a rich source of the rare gamma-linolenic acid, GLA, which is recognised, alongside other essential fatty acids, to be of major importance to the health of every organ in the body. Some readers may recall the film *Lorenzo's Oil* that featured the fight some parents undertook to make the orthodox medical profession take note of deficiency in fatty acids and their implication in health.

Evening primrose was introduced to Europe in the 17th century. Unfussy about habitat, it grows virtually anywhere. Related species have been found in China, where the oil was probably first used. All parts of the plant can be utilised and the mucilaginous root is quite nutritious. The yellow, often fragrant, flowers last a day, and are at their best in the evening before they fade and die, hence the common name. Traditionally, and hidden in its Botanic name, it has to do with hunting. Rubbing the plant on moccasins is supposed to mask the hunter's smell.

The tiny seeds are processed to yield a yellow oil that is quite unstable when exposed to light and air. Much research work was undertaken in the UK, especially in Scotland where for a while it was seen as an agricultural alternative crop. Its popularity has been superseded to some extent by Borage promoted by European suppliers. I prefer Evening Primrose to some other GLA sources. There is no 'scientific' evidence for this preference, just experience. Orthodox science does not acknowledge life force, genetic patterning, or bio-memory; therefore, sources are irrelevant. It's a bit like cheap generic drugs in the NHS. Despite the analysis, one brand seems to work better than another. Likewise I find Evening Primrose suits me better and maybe therefore suits my clients or patients.

Due to its heavy commercialisation, the refined, discoloured, deodorised versions are those normally available – very much a standard, reproducible product.

## Properties and Uses

Evening Primrose Oil is rich in unsaturated fatty acids and is one of the main sources of pure gamma-linolenic acid, thus making it an essential ingredient for dietary supplements, and an ideal agent for putting into cosmetics to provide these essential properties for skin treatment.

Therapeutic uses for GLA include treatments for blood circulation disorders and blood clot reduction, eczema and other dry skin complaints, the ageing process, nervous disorders, digestive disorders, premenstrual pains, multiple sclerosis, impotence in males, hyperactivity in children, and alcoholism. Essential fatty acids are precursors of important molecules in the immune system.

Other available uses for GLA include dietary supplements such as tablets, capsules and powders; cosmetic products, especially skin creams; infant food products; farm and domestic animal nutrition. Whilst most information concentrates on medical benefits, it is good to remember that essential fatty acids are also precursors of some cell membrane constituents. Where there is a lack of skin elasticity it should be used regularly both topically and as a supplement. This would include nail treatments where a useful combination with Myrrh essential oil can be made.

I have used Evening Primrose Oil for many skin conditions such as eczema and psoriasis, applying it in moisturising skin creams, hand and body lotions, cleansers, dispersible bath oils, and hair conditioners. In cosmetics it makes a good anti-blotch product. It works well in combination with Macadamia Oil.

Like any natural product that seems to work, there are as many (if not more) papers decrying it than extolling it. What matters is if it works for you and your patient or client, not the theory.

**Typical Fatty Acid Profile**

| C16:0 | st | Palmitic acid | 5 - 8% |
|-------|-----|---------------|--------|
| C18:0 | st | Stearic acid | 1.5% |
| C18:1 | mo | Oleic acid | 8 - 12% |
| C18:2 | pu | Linoleic acid | 65 - 75% |
| C18:3 | pu | Gamma Linolenic acid | 9 - 11% |

Unsaponifiable material between 1 – 2% includes beta-sitosterol and citrastadienol.

# Name: GOLD OF PLEASURE
## Botanic Name: *Camelina sativa*

**General Information**

Gold of Pleasure is an annual plant and a member of the Cruciferae (Brassica) family, which includes many things from mustard to cabbage. Although cultivated since prehistoric times in Northern Europe, we are probably most familiar with it as a component along with radish as a bird food for both wild and domesticated birds. Cage bird breeders, as with other bird and animal fanciers, have long known the value of oil-rich seeds to improve coat and feather.

Gold of Pleasure has been so named because of the burnished gold seeds and oil that it produces. It is also known simply as 'Camelina', but this is to be discouraged as it is so easy to confuse with the more noble oil from Camellia. It can often be found growing wild in flax fields, so it has the country name of 'false flax.'

The crude oil is clear and bright, with its distinctive golden colour, however the refined material is usually a lighter yellow. Regular production is by solvent extraction. It has a significant resistance to oxidation due to its high level of antioxidants, and evidence suggests that it has superior emollient characteristics.

## Properties and Uses

Well, if its good for the birds, it should be alright for hair care! This may well be the best use. It has been promoted as a product to replace Sperm Whale Oil and Jojoba. This is as much to do with alternative cropping in northern latitudes as anything else. This all refers to its emollient and coating properties. There are finer oils for bodywork, but such properties may be useful in wash-off products such as shampoos, where there is a need to protect from excessive dryness.

### Typical Fatty Acid Profile

| | | | |
|---|---|---|---|
| C16:0 | st | Palmitic acid | 5-6% |
| C18:0 | st | Stearic acid | 2-5% |
| C18:1 | mo | Oleic acid | 13-26% |
| C18:2 | pu | Linoleic acid | 18-24% |
| C18:3 | pu | alpha Linolenic acid | 30-40% |
| C20:0 | st | Arachidic acid | 1-2% |
| C20:1 | mo | Eicosenoic acid | 9-16% |
| C20:2 | pu | Eicosadienoic acid | 1-2.0% |
| C22:1 | mo | Erucic acid | 0-4% |

# Name: GOURD or PUMPKIN OIL
## Botanic Name: *Cucurbita pepo*

### General Information

The gourd referred to here comes from the continent of the Americas. Its heartlands are the dry areas of Mexico and Texas. Introduced into Europe in the 16th century, it was one of the first vegetables to have been brought back from the New World. Species of gourds are, however, found all over the world; in Africa, the Far East, and Central Asia. It is an annual garden vegetable with a very long, creeping, hollow, hairy stem, and wide leaves bristling with rough hairs. The flowers are large, yellow, and funnel-shaped. The fruit is bulky, smooth or warty – depending on the species – and contains many seeds in a spongy pulp. It is reminiscent of melons, pumpkins, and marrows, and like them belongs to the Cucurbitaceae family. Marrow and Pumpkin, Cucurbita maxima are close enough to have similar properties, and the latter yields a similar oil.

The flesh and the whitish flat seed have frequently been used in medicine. Given its many seeds, gourd symbolises abundance and is also a symbol of regeneration. Taoists regard it as a food of immortality; and in some African societies, the seeds are eaten and regarded as symbols of intelligence. In Thai mythology, celestial gourds, real horns of plenty, contained not only human species, but also all the varieties of rice and the handbook of secret sciences.

### Properties and Uses

Most of us are familiar with gourds being used as some sort of drinking vessel or cup. Dioscorides recommended drinking wine that had remained in a freshly emptied gourd as a laxative. The Arabs used the sap to relieve headaches, and it has been reported that a peasant recovered from a frenzy after receiving a treatment in the form of slices of gourd, cucumber, and melon applied to his head! A cooling down treatment? There are many other great virtues allotted to gourd, including a preparation made from the seeds as a throat emulsion for colds and inflamed digestive tracts, and also an efficient remedy against tapeworm.

Gourd Oil has been used to treat bladder infections; and the ground seeds, when mixed with honey or milk, have a soothing effect in cases of painful urination. Gourd has also been important since ancient times as a food during recovery or during illness, being easy to digest and therefore highly recommended for delicate stomachs.

Virgin Gourd Seed Oil has fine emollient and restructuring properties and is used in hand and body products, and face creams for dry, damaged, and mature skin. There is no proportion limit for the use of Gourd Seed Oil in cosmetic compounds as it is very safe. It can be recommended for hand care products.

**Typical Fatty Acid Profile**

| C16:0 | st | Palmitic acid | 13 - 15% |
|-------|-----|---------------|----------|
| C18:0 | st | Stearic acid | 6% |
| C18:1 | mo | Oleic acid | 35 - 47% |
| C18:2 | pu | Linoleic acid | 30 - 45% |

The unsaponifiable material content is at least 2%.

# Name: GRAPE SEED OIL
Botanic Name:  *Vitis vinifera*

## General Information
Grape is one of the most ancient traditional cultivated plants. All wine-growing countries, mainly located on the Mediterranean basin, have been known to take advantage of the products derived from the vine. A lot could be said about wine – books! This book is about oils, and there is no particular historic

use of this material due to the technology needed to obtain the oil. Grape seeds only contain between 5% and 20% of lipids, depending upon variety, so a great deal of pressure and heat (additional or from the unheated, cold press) is needed to generate the oil that needs a lot of refining to make it acceptable. It became popular in Aromatherapy because, being a by-product from waste, it was cheap and seemed to have a lot going for it on paper. It is typically a heavily promoted European product, although some is manufactured in California.

Usually the crude oil is dark-coloured, but after refining varies from colourless to greenish. The profile can be highly variable depending upon variety and manufacturer.

## Properties and Uses

The refined Grape Seed oil is used in food for seasoning and frying. It is almost tasteless with little or no odour. There are several industrial applications such as for fine machine oils. The soap industry uses it for the manufacture of liquid soaps. Its high content of linoleic acid gives it a health food nutritional profile.

Due to its low price and promotion by toiletry companies, it became popular amongst some Aromatherapists, almost a standard. This is a shame, for when the oil is set against a good virgin Almond, Apricot or Walnut, it has little to commend it. Like many highly processed oils, it has a chemical profile that highlights certain useful components, and it does provide slippage. The 'eco' claim to profitably use waste has to be set against the energy needed to produce it. At the time of writing, new cold pressed material is said to be on offer – always check out what you are really being sold.

If making a cosmetic range for economy, this oil is ideal as a filler. It fulfils the basic criteria of having film-forming virtues and emollient properties. It is an ideal medium to upgrade from white mineral oil, which it readily replaces; hence its popularity with Massage therapy, rather than true Aromatherapy where more care in the choice of active materials is expected. It is used in cosmetic preparations for its soothing and calming properties, and by moisture retention prevents skin ageing.

**Typical Fatty Acid Profile**

| | | | |
|---|---|---|---|
| C16:0 | st | Palmitic acid | 5 - 11% |
| C16:1 | mo | Palmitoleic acid | 0.5% |
| C18:0 | st | Stearic acid | 3 - 6% |
| C18:1 | mo | Oleic acid | 12 - 28% |
| C18:2 | pu | Linoleic acid | 58 - 78% |

Additional unsaponifiable elements vary between 0.8 to 1.5%, being mainly phenols and steroids.

# Name: HAZELNUT OIL
**Botanic Name:** *Corylus avellana*

## General Information

Filberts, Cobnuts and the French Noisette are all one and the same. Hazelnut trees grow almost everywhere in Europe, but especially in the Mediterranean and Black Sea areas where fruit is extensively cultivated. They are found in many British hedgerows and copses, and were once a staple winter food for both animals and humans. The Latin name derives from the shape of the seed – a little 'helmet'.

My first recollection is not of the nuts but the male flowers – the long yellow catkins, harbingers of early Spring. With such a long use it is hardly surprising that many folk tales exist around it. The nuts are good for impotence, according to Hildegarde of Bingen. Folk references often refer to its usefulness for bilious problems – there is often some truth in folk remedies. Divining rods and wands are made from the living wood. It is in cakes and confectionary that it excels.

Typically oil bearing, it maintains about 40% of its weight in oil and is therefore readily cold pressed, yielding a dark yellow oil with distinct taste and typical odour Watch out for different grades, some for food, some for cosmetics, etc. Refining is common for the cosmetic industry and other applications. The oil is lighter in colour. The starting material, too, may be different, perhaps mouldy and worm-ridden. This is certainly a consideration if you, the user, are committed to principles of life force or vitality. The same holds true for many food nuts. You get what you pay for. Cooking oil is, however, often drawn from roasted nuts to improve flavour, so do not confuse food grade starting material with the end results.

## Properties and Uses

Hazelnut Oil is made from the fruit of the tree. It is quite similar to Sweet Almond Oil in composition and stability, and also has the same properties. However, the diffusion and penetration powers seem to be far greater than in Sweet Almond Oil. It contains vitamins A, B, and is rich in E. This oil is highly recommended as a carrier oil because of its ability to penetrate the epidermis without leaving the skin greasy. Certainly it demonstrates softening properties, but I rarely use it alone except in hair care. Dry hair responds well to a Hazel Oil soak especially when combined with a stimulating essential oil. It combines well with its cousin Sweet Almond.

The slightly fatty or rich Hazelnut Oil provides very interesting restructuring properties on the skin, and is used in a wide range of finished skin care products such as body creams, hand creams, cleansers, sun oils and creams, massage oils, lipsticks, and foam baths. Due to its diffusive characteristics it prevents dehydration of the skin, and is particularly recommended for sensitive skin and baby skin, leaving it smooth and soft.

Combined with Sesame, and with the addition of Calendula Herbal Oil or phytol, it makes an excellent after-sun oil. There are studies that show a sun filter effect, so it may be used alongside other sun filter products. If making a commercial preparation, be especially careful about filter claims. Accepted or permitted sunscreens, bar some minerals, are all of synthetic origin, but may be reinforced by natural materials such as Hazelnut Oil.

**Typical Fatty Acid Profile**

| C16:0 | st | Palmitic acid | 4 - 9% |
|-------|-----|------------------|-------------|
| C16:1 | mo | Palmitoleic acid | 0.1% - 0.8% |
| C18:0 | st | Stearic acid | 1 - 4% |
| C18:1 | mo | Oleic acid | 71 - 87% |
| C18:2 | pu | Linoleic acid | 7 - 18% |

A good keeping oil, compared to some, as the unsaponifiable content, 0.3% - 1%, is richest in alpha tocopherol.

# Name: HEMP OIL
**Botanic Name:** *Cannabis sativa*

## General Information

Cannabis Oil suffers from the political controversy surrounding the drug. As a result, it suffers on the one hand from a stigma, and on the other, from being promoted to soften views on the drug itself. The oil has no psychotropic use and contains no actives of that nature for two or three reasons. The varieties grown for oil yield little or no resin, the source of the drug, and the seed used is sterilised to stop germination (those seeking to promote this oil often have ideas related to life force and vitalism so this should be noted as a literal dead end) prior to cold-pressing.

The word 'sativa' loosely means 'useful'; and cannabis is, could be, and has been very useful. Due to its association with drugs, we forget that it was introduced to Britain by the Romans and cultivated in west Dorset and Devon for centuries. The fibres were the backbone of the Bridport rope making industry, destined for the English navy and Crewkerne, famous for its canvas sails. True 'canvas' (cannabis) is also made from these versatile fibres. The nearest most of us will come to hemp these days is in birdseed. Not only is it nutritious, but also good for improving the appearance of feathers.

## Properties and Uses

Cannabis is being recognised as medicinally beneficial to cancer patients suffering from chemotherapy nausea, and to multiple sclerosis sufferers. Our interest is in the oil, and the reference to feathers would suggest that in human use, hair and nails would seem the best targets. It could be used as a culinary oil and has a bland taste not unlike sunflower.

The oil is rich in the essential fatty acids and in the desirable Omega 3's and GLA. For topical application it has a behaviour like that of Olive Oil, and it would seem a good idea to blend with a lighter substance, such as Apricot Kernel, to make it workable. For hair care, massaging in and leaving on for an hour prior to washing out might be practical, especially for those with weak and tired, heat or perm damaged hair. A combination with Jojoba would be a good idea. It can also be massaged into the nail bed for stronger and fast growing nails.

### Typical Fatty Acid Profile

| | | | |
|---|---|---|---|
| C16:0 | st | Palmitic acid | 5% |
| C18:0 | st | Stearic acid | 2% |
| C18:1 | mo | Oleic acid | 10 – 15% |
| C18:2 | pu | Linoleic acid | 50 – 60% |
| C18:3 | pu | Linolenic acid | 25 – 30% |

Name: JOJOBA OIL
Botanic Name: *Simmondsia chinensis*

## General Information

Like many things originating from the US, Jojoba was hailed as one of Nature's miracles. Certainly, there are a lot of exaggerated claims for Jojoba but it genuinely does offer some unique properties. Like aloe vera, though, there are many types available having different end-uses. Jojoba is a wild evergreen shrub found in the Sonora Desert in the southwestern United States and throughout the dry lands of Mexico. Today it is cultivated in many arid areas from Israel to South America. It can withstand the extreme temperatures of the deserts and, while the shrub itself will withstand one year without any rain, the flower and seeds need small amounts of moisture.

Jojoba comes under that category of truly oil bearing. The seed yields up to 60% of itself as oil. The Native Americans have always used jojoba oil as a cooking oil and for hair care. They have also used it as a healing agent, even in cancer care. The best golden oil is extracted from the jojoba bean by cold pressure and, in its crude form, is a liquid wax and not an oil. It can be found hydrogenated, and forms the basis of balms and stick products.

The name is of native origin and the plant itself gave a drink that encouraged visions. The beverage was snorted through the nose to achieve a trancelike state.

## Properties and Uses

The composition of Jojoba Oil is similar to, and better than, the Sperm Whale Oil.

Because of its high compatibility with the skin, Jojoba Oil is considered to be a very efficient component in skin care products, and as an anti-ageing factor or active, so the Aromatherapist might make this a standard inclusive component of any facial blend or composition. It is used widely in hair shampoos and conditioners, soaps, face and body creams and lotions, sunning products, and lipsticks.

This 'substance' is best termed a wax. It hardly contains any triglycerides but is a combination of esters and fatty alcohols. In use, it can be temperature sensitive (i.e. hardening when cold) and this is a consideration when making creams for different climatic conditions. It is ideal for chapped hands and skin, or for those plagued by chilblains.

Whilst its traditional use is protective for skin in dry conditions, it should be realised this is also an ideal oil for sebum control or for those prone to oily skin. Containing anti- inflammatory elements, it can be used for acne sufferers in combination with other vegetable oils and essential oils. It also becomes useful for other blends that are designed to ease inflammatory articular or joint pains such as in cases of arthritis.

Jojoba Oil is also used in the pharmaceutical industry in skin preparations for eczema, dandruff, acne, etc. The oil has tremendous resistance to oxidation so is easy to use and store.

### Typical Fatty Acid Profile

| | | | |
|---|---|---|---|
| C16:0 | st | Palmitic acid | 0 - 2% |
| C18:1 | mo | Oleic acid | 10 - 13% |
| C20:1 | mo | Eicosenoic acid | 66 - 71% |
| C22:0 | st | Behenic acid | 0 - 1% |
| C22:1 | mo | Docosenoic acid | 14 - 20% |

The fatty alcohols present, in descending order of importance are: eicosanol, docosanol, tetracosanol, octadecanol, and other traces.

# Name: KIWIFRUIT SEED OIL
Botanic Name: *Actinidia chinensis Planch.*


## General Information

Kiwifruits are Chinese Himalayan in origin and known in some quarters as the 'Chinese gooseberry'. Today, the main centre of commercial cultivation is New Zealand. The name 'Kiwi' belongs, first and foremost, to a small, shy, wingless bird that lives in the dark forests of New Zealand, eating worms by moonlight! The second largest world producer of Kiwifruits is southern France.

The Kiwi is a climbing vine with a woody stem, heart-shaped leaves, and gorgeous creamy white flowers. The fruit is capsule-shaped with a thin, fuzzy, leathery skin, and green, juicy flesh spotted with numerous tiny, black seeds. This flesh is a concentrate of vitamin C, outdoing Lemon but not as good as Rose Hip. The seeds provide an oil that is rich in essential fatty acids and vitamin E.

In practice, this is another of the fashionable seed oils promoted either by the health food or cosmetic industries. The downside for all these seed types is the means of manufacture. Nevertheless, anything from vegetable origin has to be an improvement on mineral oil, if only for ecological reasons.


## Properties and Uses

The oil is a pale yellow colour, of light viscosity, and comes in a refined format. In massage it is very easy to work with, providing good slippage without an apparent film-forming characteristic. It handles very similarly to baby oil. It is ideally suited to professional pharmaceutical and health products, and cosmetic applications.

It is used to fortify and enhance various health foods that support cell growth, particularly nervous and eye tissue. Its skin care attributes suggest it for straightforward body massage oils. Additionally, the concentration in essential fatty acids means it is of value in anti-wrinkle creams, but its use

133

would span all skin types. It would be a valuable addition to moisturisers. Caution should be exercised in storage as it not a good keeping oil.

### Typical Fatty Acid Profile

| | | | |
|---|---|---|---|
| C16:0 | st | Palmitic acid | 6% |
| C18::0 | st | Stearic acid | 2% |
| C18:1 | mo | Oleic acid | 13% |
| C18:2 | pu | Linoleic acid | 16% |
| C18:3 | pu | alpha Linolenic acid | 63% |

## Name: KUKUI NUT OIL
### Botanic Name: *Aleurites moluccana*

### General Information

This is one of the glories of the South Seas, and a most useful and fine oil. In 1959, the Kukui Nut tree became the official state tree of Hawaii. It is thought that the first Polynesian settlers introduced the species, but pollen evidence suggests that it is a native. It grows well on the volcanic soils.

The Kukui tree, which grows on the lower slopes of the mountains, has light, beautifully coloured foliage, and the silver-greyish powder on its leaves makes it quite easy to spot in the forest. The small, white but green-tinged flowers are often incorporated along with the leaves in the floral leis. The soot from the shell husk, when burnt, was used as a colorant in tattoos. The nuts are high in oil, and when skewered burn as brightly as torches. It's a very versatile tree with many uses.

The fruit has a hard, green covering of about a quarter of an inch thick, inside of which are two hard, stone-like, wrinkled nuts. When young, the shell of the nut is white, but as it matures it turns brown and then black. Hundreds of years ago, the Hawaiians discovered that when the shells were removed from the nuts, a clear oil could be pressed out if the kernels were lightly roasted. This oil was found to be an excellent skin penetrating oil and, when smoothed on the skin, it soothed and softened sunburns and irritations. Newborn babies were bathed in this easily absorbed and fine oil.

## Properties and Uses

The light yellow Kukui Nut Oil is definitely a first choice ingredient used on its own or in combination. Local uses relate it closely to baby care and skin care. This oil is high in essential fatty acids vital to the metabolism of healthy skin. Kukui Nut Oil, when tested, was found to rank among the best of the polyunsaturated essential oils, unique in many of its properties for the preparation of skin and hair care products. It has a reputation for being excellent for the treatment of superficial burns, chapped skin and some minor skin abrasions.

In its homeland, you will not go far without finding numerous testimonials as to its efficacy for Psoriasis. It slows water loss, softens scales, and importantly, is very quickly absorbed. Eczema sufferers, including children, are said to benefit from using Kukui in a milk or cream base, or blended alone with vitamin E. Reports indicate it to be effective even for long-term hydrocortisone users. Similarly, those who experience after-shower itch, and those with dry or irritated skin, will love Kukui. In cancer care where radiation treatment has been used, the skin is often red, dry, burned. Kukui has been used to effectively remedy this condition. Research continues at the Hawaiian Agricultural Research Centre on transepidermal water loss and Kukui.

Not least, consideration should be given to its anti-ageing properties, which combine well with its softening activity. The oil makes an excellent nutritive massage oil for mature skins, and provides the therapist with good touch and feel characteristics. It is one of my favourites.

## Typical Fatty Acid Profile

| | | | |
|---|---|---|---|
| C16:0 | st | Palmitic acid | 6% |
| C16:1 | mo | Palmitoleic acid | 0.1% |
| C18:0 | st | Stearic acid | 0.3% |

| C18:1 | mo | Oleic acid | 20% |
|-------|-----|----------------|-------|
| C18:2 | pu | Linoleic acid | 42% |
| C18:3 | pu | Linolenic | 29% |
| C20:1 | mo | Eicosenoic acid | 0.?? |

## Name: MACADAMIA NUT OIL
Botanic Name: *Macadamia ternifolia*

### General Information

The Macadamia Nut tree is indigenous to the Brisbane area on the Australian east coast. It is known locally as 'bush nut' or 'Queensland nut'. Although Australian botanists discovered and named the Macadamia Nut tree more than 125 years ago, the species was not exploited until the 1950's. The species was introduced into Hawaii in 1881, and now Hawaii is the largest producer of Macadamia nuts in the world. Macadamia nuts are delicious to eat and the oil makes an excellent salad dressing or bread dip.

In Hawaii, flowering normally occurs between November and February, and the harvesting period starts around August of the following year and continues for six months. The flowers are usually a creamy white. When they reach maturity the nuts usually drop from the trees, and they are then transported to a husking station where the husks are stripped off as soon as possible to minimise the loss of quality. The nuts are then sent in their shells to factories where they are placed in drying bins. Careful monitoring of internal kernel moisture and drying temperatures is necessary. The oil is generally cold pressed.

## Properties and Uses

Macadamia Nut Oil is a pale coloured, low-odour oil that makes a superior massage oil. It sinks into the skin rapidly but still provides a workable film. The overall profile is not so far from human sebum. Macadamia has a very high content of palmitoleic acid. This is rare in vegetable oils, sources usually being fish oils. Palmitoleic acid is vital to delaying skin and cell ageing. It is noticed that at the menopause, the skin has a sharp reduction in this fatty acid. Macadamia could be incorporated in all anti-ageing regimes or products. The oil is easily emulsified and freely soluble in most other oils, blending well. It has a superior spreading co-efficiency, is self-stabilising, and requires few or no antioxidants. All these properties make this oil an excellent natural formulation product in addition to its clear therapeutic value to skin.

Clearly a monounsaturated oil, Macadamia would be of nutritional benefit for those concerned with circulation problems. Its antioxidant properties will also be of significance for those with arterial disease.

Best described as a nourishing oil, it will not only support moisturisation, and provide restructuring properties, but protect cell lipids from rancidity – peroxidation. Its practical value is for mature skins, but it would be effective in eye gels and other delicate skin areas.

### Typical Fatty Acid Profile

| | | | |
|---|---|---|---|
| C12:0 | st | Lauric acid | Traces |
| C14:0 | st | Myristic acid | 0.4 - 1.6% |
| C16:0 | st | Palmitic acid | 7 - 10% |
| C16:1 | mo | Palmitoleic acid | 16 - 23% |
| C18:0 | st | Stearic acid | 1.5 - 5% |
| C18:1 | mo | Oleic acid | 54 - 63% |
| C18:2 | pu | Linoleic acid | 1 - 3% |
| C20:0 | st | Arachidic acid | 1.5 - 3% |
| C20:1 | mo | Eicosenoic acid | 1 - 3% |

# Name: MEADOW FOAM OIL
Botanic Name: *Limnanthes alba*

## General Information

Meadow Foam is another of those soft sounding names that attract us. It is a herbaceous winter annual plant native to northern California and the West Coast of the USA, and up into Canada. It is valued for the high quality oil contained in its seed. The common name 'Meadow Foam' refers to the billowing ocean appearance of the cream white flowers in the huge growing lands of the US. It is becoming another oil crop in Europe. As with many of these seed oils, it requires refinement, although the oil content can be quite high, as much as 25% by weight but still short of the more noble and traditional oil bearing seeds.

## Properties and Uses

A versatile industrial refined raw material, Meadow Foam Oil has many applications in cosmetics, lubricants, waxes, polymers, surfactants, water repellents, and in textile and leather manufacturing. For cosmetic purposes, it is easily converted into a liquid wax similar to Jojoba, and a solid wax similar to Carnauba and Candelilla. It is a very stable oil with a high tocopherol content. It would seem suited to therapists in hot climes where the keeping properties of oils are dubious. If added to more sensitive oils, it would contribute to their stability.

In common with all oils, it has emollient properties and may be considered for incorporating into rich creams with more of a heavy texture. This would be a good base for a gardeners' cream or working-hand creams due to its substantive texture.

### Typical Fatty Acid Profile

| | | | |
|---|---|---|---|
| C20:1 | mo | Eicosenoic acid | 62% |
| C22:1 | mo | Erucic acid | 16% |
| C22:2 | pu | Docosadienoic acid | 17% |

# Name: MILK THISTLE OIL
Botanic Name: *Silybum marianum Gaertn.*

## General Information

A legend of the Middle Ages tells us of the Virgin Mary who, wishing to protect Jesus, chose to put him under thistle leaves in order to hide him from the
Roman soldiers. Presumably, they didn't want to get pricked. She is said to
have leant forwards and some drops of her milk fell on the thistles around
her, leaving white strips on the leaves. This species of thistle has been called
'Milk Thistle' since then.

Milk Thistle grows wild on uncultivated areas in the South of France,
central and southern Europe, Western Asia, and North Africa. It belongs to
the Asteraceae family, and is a biennial plant with a strong stem that bears
large, green, shiny leaves with thorny lobes and white veins. The solitary ter-
minal flower heads are made up of purple tubule flowers surrounded by
thorny scales. The seed is black, shiny, and wrinkled; it's a common weed. It
was once used as a vegetable, and carries the country name of 'Wild Artichoke'.
The Milk Thistle Oil is obtained from the seed by pressure and solvent and
is refined. The seeds contain up to 30% lipids. It is greenish-yellow in colour,
and rich in essential fatty acids.

## Properties and Uses

The herb is renowned for its application to those who suffer from liver disease. It is a detoxifying herb. The oil should contain a specific group of
flavonoids including a flavoligan called 'silymarine'. This gives the plant its
hepatic cell protective effect as well as antioxidant properties.

Milk Thistle Oil for topical use is essentially a formulation ingredient.
It has excellent skin conditioning and restructuring properties. The oil also
contains steroids needed for skin health and function. Use it where the
underlying structure is deteriorating and/or the skin is devitalised and damaged. Inclusion in detoxifying massage oils or in cellulite treatment should
always be considered.

**Typical Fatty Acid Profile**

| | | | |
|---|---|---|---|
| C16:0 | st | Palmitic acid | 8% |
| C18:0 | st | Stearic acid | 5% |
| C18:1 | mo | Oleic acid | 22% |
| C18:2 | pu | Linoleic acid | 57% |
| C18:3 | pu | Linolenic acid | 0.3% |
| C20:0 | st | Arachidic | 3% |
| C20:1 | mo | Eicosenoic acid | 1% |
| C22:0 | st | Behenic acid | 2% |
| C24:0 | st | Tetracosanoic acid | 0.6% |

The unsaponifiable content includes a rich number of steroids, mainly stigmasterol and sitosterol, along with tocopherols.

# Name: MONOI OIL
**Botanic Name:** *C.nucifera with Gardenia tahitensis*

## General Information

Rooted in cultural and religious traditions, the Monoi Oil has always been used by the French Polynesians for medicinal and cosmetic purposes. It is notably reputed for the protection it gives both to the skin and hair against the sun and sea salt. The anglicised word Monoi has a Tahitian origin and simply means 'perfumed oil.'

In conformity with local traditions, true Monoi Oil is obtained by a ten-day maceration of ten Tiare flowers (Tahitian Gardenia) in a given quantity of Coprah or Coconut Oil. The real benefits of the oil can then best be ascribed to the activity of Coconut Oil. The cost of the oil is said to vary by the number of flowers used. Modern production shortens the process by adding a percentage of real gardenia absolute to the oil. It takes 40,000 flowers to make one kilo of absolute, all picked by hand! Price variation is due to the amount of absolute used. Sadly, today most 'Monoi' is perfumed by synthetic fragrances having quite harsh and dominant smells. Monoi can also be found perfumed with the warm aroma of Frangipani flowers and the sweet smell of Vanilla pods. In all cases, natural macerations or absolutes should be sought where possible, with their more delicate and less sickly fragrances.

The Tiare shrub is a small tree with stiff branches, shiny leaves, and bright, white, star-shaped flowers with a strong and sweet perfume. These flowers are often placed above the ear of the Tahitian women, fixed in their hair or shaped into a flowery crown. The Tiare is the basic ornament of the Vahine and dancers of Tahiti; in fact, it is the symbol of Tahiti.

The Coprah Oil comes from the dried coconut pulp. Production is a long process involving removal of the coconut fibres, breaking the nuts to be dried either in the sun or in drying ovens, and finally sorting for best use.

## Properties and Uses

Monoi Oil has a faint yellow colour and has moisturising and nourishing properties. It can be used neat as a skin care or body oil. Aromatherapists, in practice, have found it gives the skin a soft and silky quality. I use it as my general massage oil when no particular benefit is required other than sheer pleasure! It is also recommended for hair care because it brings suppleness and sheen to the hair; and, of course, is makes a very good after-sun product as it protects both skin and hair against dryness due to sun and salty sea.

### Typical Fatty Acid Profile

It has the same fatty acid profile as Coconut Oil.

| C8:0 | st | Caprylic acid | 6 - 10% |
|------|-----|---------------|---------|
| C10:0 | st | Capric acid | 5 - 10% |
| C12:0 | st | Lauric acid | 39 - 54% |
| C14:0 | st | Myristic acid | 15 - 23% |

| C16:0 | st | Palmitic acid | 6 - 11% |
| C18:0 | st | Stearic acid | 1 - 4% |
| C18:1 | mo | Oleic acid | 4 - 11% |
| C18:2 | pu | Linoleic acid | 1 - 2% |

Unsaponifiables are present at a rate of between 0.6 - 1.5%.

## Name: MORINGA OIL
Botanic Name: *Moringa oleifera*

### General Information

This oil ranks as one of the most ancient known to mankind. Before alcohol was known, it was the material in which all perfumes were diluted. When ancient texts refer to 'perfumed oil', this was it! It is also known as 'Oil of Ben'. Probably originating in the foothills of the Himalayas, Moringa spread to three continents. It grows in semi-arid conditions and has found its main uses in Africa, especially in the perfume centres of Egypt. Its uses are not limited to the oil: it is used in medicine, and its young seed pods as foodstuff. The English name 'Horseradish Tree' is most unattractive, and the tree has nothing to do with the vegetable. The pods are hand picked and cold pressed. Industrial uses are found for its esters in cosmetics.

### Properties and Uses

Aromatherapists have found this to be a particularly useful oil for very dry skin and impure or acne prone skin. It is taken up immediately and has a dry touch and feel. Its traditional use of carrying essential oils, the making of perfume oils, is still relevant and it combines well with balm bases and gel cream perfume bases. For an ultra rich, nutritive body or face massage, I combine it with Macadamia Oil, also noted for its benefit to mature skin. Moringa at 60% and Macadamia – the balance seems to work well.

Its reputation is built upon its resistance to oxidation. This was so important when storing oils in ancient times. Today this benefit also holds true, but now we also understand Moringa contributes important antioxidant components to anti-ageing treatments. It outperforms Coconut, Castor and Sunflower, the normal star performers, and makes Jojoba, Squalene, and Macadamia poor performers when these are normally regarded as superior to most.

### Typical Fatty Acid Profile

| | | | |
|---|---|---|---|
| C14:0 | st | Myristic acid | 0.1% |
| C16:0 | st | Palmitic acid | 5.8% |
| C16:1 | mo | Palmitoleic acid | 1.4% |
| C18:0 | st | Stearic acid | 6.0% |
| C18:1 | mo | Oleic acid | 65% |
| C18:2 | pu | Linoleic acid | 0.6% |
| C20:0 | st | Arachidic acid | 3.8% |
| C20:1 | mo | Eicosenoic acid | 2.0% |
| C22:0 | st | Behenic acid | 6.3% |
| C24:0 | st | Lignocric acid | 0.7% |

# Name: NEEM OIL
Botanic Name: *Azadirachta indica*

## General Information

Neem or Margosa has become popular on the wave of interest in Ayurvedic medicine. Its common name is 'Persian Lilac'. It has pretty, fragrant lilac flowers and I first came across it whilst in Israel. Taking a seed home, it grew well in south-west England and, although known as an Indian tree, it is widespread throughout the world.

Many Indian legends are associated with the tree, considered sacred from ancient times. In Hindu mythology, when Garuda the sacred bird took Amrita, the elixir of life, to heaven, a few drops fell to earth and landed on the Neem tree giving its medicinal properties.

It has become over promoted and has achieved miracle status. This should not discourage you from using it. Ignorance by importers has led to confusion between Neem Seed Oil and an oil extract of the leaves. Virgin cold pressed Neem Seed Oil, some even wild crafted, is available and the sort best suited to Aromatherapy. The oil is dark and has a pungent and unpleasant odour, slightly sulphurous with a bitter taste.

## Properties and Uses

Neem Oil contains a constituent called Azadirachtin, which has strong anti-microbial activity. It also has insecticide properties, and is used as a natural pesticide against many bugs in the garden, as well as being used commercially. In the materia medica of the Aromatherapist, it can frequently be combined with essential oils for wounds, cuts, and scrapes. It has excellent anti-fungal activity so is useful against athlete's foot. Its many applications include viral and bacterial infections manifest on the skin, such as chicken pox. It is an immune stimulant. Direct application against head lice is effective. It can also be used in animal health care.

144

For topical use it can be used neat in many applications. The strong odour and colour can be disguised and its effects enhanced by using a good base cream or lotion, along with appropriate essential oils.

### Typical Fatty Acid Profile

| C16:0 | st | Palmitic acid | 18% |
|-------|-----|----------------|-----|
| C18:0 | st | Stearic acid | 15% |
| C18:1 | mo | Oleic acid | 50% |
| C18:2 | pu | Linoleic acid | 13% |
| C20:0 | st | Arachidic acid | 2% |

# Name: OLIVE OIL
Botanic Name:  *Olea europaea*

## General Information

The Olive tree is a cultivated evergreen tree, gnarled with a greyish bark and silvery green leaves. It always looks old even if quite young. This befits its ancient heritage. Along with honey, mead, beer, and milk, Olive Oil ranks as the stuff of ancient civilisation. Legend states that in a contest of the gods, Pallas Athene was awarded the prize for the most useful gift. She presented the olive to Zeus. Greek and Roman literature are full of references to the olive and its oil. It is native to the Near East and is widely found in Italy, Spain, Portugal, Greece, Tunisia, Morocco, and Syria.

The tree does well on little moisture but is quite prone to cold. Olives bloom in late spring with clusters of white flowers. The fruit is small and green, and then red becoming black when ripened. Lipogenesis turns the fruit acids and sugars to oil. It is the flesh that is used to obtain the oil, not the stone or seed. The degree of ripeness determines the taste of the oil.

In Europe, Olive Oil is the primary culinary oil. Food buffs, as with wine, get very excited about the different tastes and qualities of Olive Oil. This is a lesson that can be applied to all oils, and is food for thought about the real benefit of highly processed oil. Cold pressed extra virgin is the best available. Colour varies according to the ripeness of the olive used, from deep green to light yellow. Many qualities exist and again, as a lesson on other oils, they are blended to a price, say refined with virgin etc. As an international commodity, there are appropriate brands magically maintaining the same colour and taste year after year, and small local producers so proud of this year's unique crop and taste. Olive Oil appreciation is an art form!

**Properties and Uses**

Olive Oil is used primarily in cooking and in salad dressings and these are the best ways to receive its health benefits. The so-called Mediterranean diet, rich in Olive Oil, is recommended for those with heart conditions. Once again, monounsaturates without cholesterol are indicated as beneficial. It reduces gastric acidity and has a mild laxative effect, plus it plays a role in stimulating bile secretion.

It is a little heavy and sticky for general massage work although some enjoy it. A good oil does carry a strong odour. Traditionally, Olive Oil is used for treating skin problems and for soaking nails to improve their strength. It is a general emollient and has anti-inflammatory properties, and is a useful ingredient in sun protection products and where the skin has been irritated by bites, stings or by reaction to plants such as nettles.

Olive Oil has been used for treating burns; dermatitis, especially eczema and psoriasis; and sensitive and chapped skin. It is not a favoured oil in Aromatherapy, and I think its best use is as a formulation ingredient in medium touch creams. There has been some suggestions about using compresses with AIDS victims.

It is *the primary food oil* and should form part of any healthy diet.

**Typical Fatty Acid Profile**

| | | | |
|---|---|---|---|
| C18:1 | mo | Oleic acid | 60 - 85% |
| C18:2 | pu | Linoleic acid | 9 - 14% |
| C18:3 | pu | Linolenic acid | 1% |

# Name: PALM and Palm Kernel OIL
**Botanic Name:** *Elaeis guineensis*

## General Information

The Palm tree comes from Guinea, from where it was taken to the Americas by the slaves and their traders. It is nowadays cultivated also in Malaysia, Indonesia, Brazil, and all over the western coast of Africa.

The Palm tree is a symbol of sun, victory, wealth, strength, and resistance. Dreaming of a Palm tree is a sign of wealth and good luck. According to legend, along with the olive tree, the palm tree was also believed to have been brought into Greece by Heracles when he returned from Hades. Palm branches were spread at his feet when Jesus entered Jerusalem. According to Pliny the Elder, the Delos palm tree dates back to Apollo. In Sicily, a ritual formula is spoken while cutting three palm leaves in order to get rid of witches!

The palm tree is 15 to 30 metres high, with a straight cylindrical trunk. It has large, thin pinnate leaves and it grows bulky bunches of one to two thousand reddish-yellow, plum-like, fleshy, oval-shaped fruits, from which the oil is extracted. The colour varies from yellow to reddish depending upon the carotenes present. The kernel or seed also yields a light yellow oil. The kernel oil is solid in northern climes, the palm oil less so but still prone to solidification at lower temperatures. These oils are huge business and most go into the soap and detergent industries.

## Properties and Uses

Like Olive and Avocado, Palm Oil can be said to be nut free, the oil coming from the flesh. Palm Oil is assigned some important regenerative properties due to its content of carotenoids, which promote vitamin A activity in the skin and aid cell regeneration. Like all oils rich in essential fatty acids, it has a restructuring activity, reinforces the skin's protective barrier and helps to maintain a moist and healthy skin. Aromatherapists can build some interesting skin care products around this stable oil.

Palm Oil is used in cosmetics, usually in hair conditioners; massage oils; hand creams; damaged, tired or mature skin treatment creams, sun preparations, and lip balms. Palm Kernel Oil, resembling coconut, finds its main use in industry.

### Typical Fatty Acid Profile

| | | | |
|---|---|---|---|
| C16:0 | st | Palmitic acid | 43 - 45% |
| C18:0 | st | Stearic acid | 4 - 5% |
| C18:1 | mo | Oleic acid | 38 - 41% |
| C18:2 | pu | Linoleic acid | 9 - 11% |

Containing up to 1.2% unsaponifiables, particularly alpha and beta carotenes, these vitamin A precursors can contribute to a valuable product.

### Palm Kernel Oil

| | | | |
|---|---|---|---|
| C8:0 | st | Caprylic acid | 2 - 6% |
| C10:0 | st | Capric acid | 3 - 5% |
| C12:0 | st | Lauric acid | 40 - 55% |
| C14:0 | st | Myristic acid | 14 - 18% |
| C16:0 | st | Palmitic acid | 6 - 10% |
| C18:1 | mo | Oleic acid | 12 - 20% |

# Name: PASSION FRUIT or FLOWER OIL
Botanic Name: *Passiflora incarnata*


## General Information

Although generally known as Passion Flower Oil, strictly speaking this oil comes from the fruit. Unscrupulous sellers may use this opportunity to sell a herbal oil or maceration instead of the real or genuine seed oil. There are many 'amateur' suppliers in Aromatherapy who do not have a genuine interest in the materials they sell and so mistakes are made. Passion fruit is a tropical climbing plant well known to British gardeners. The fruits range from yellow to dark red to crimson. Originally from South America, the plant was used by the Mayans as an eye salve. In herbal medicine, the flower has sedative properties.

The Spanish invaders used the shape and elements of the plant to teach the Christian doctrine of the Passion of Jesus, hence its common name. As a talisman, it was said to bring peace and, in the language of flowers, to represent bitter love. The fruit is edible and is used to flavour everything from ice cream to jam.


## Properties and Uses

The oil is only found in refined form and may be categorised as a fashion oil. The colour is a pale yellow and it makes a pleasant massage oil, light and practical for face massage and for those who do not like a 'greasy' feel. It is readily absorbed but workable.

The high content in polyunsaturates make this a good formulation ingredient for moisturising preparations. Due to its handling characteristics, it lends itself to lotions and milks.


### Typical Fatty Acid Profile

| | | | |
|---|---|---|---|
| C14:0 | st | Myristic acid | 0.1% |
| C16:0 | st | Palmitic acid | 8.5 - 10% |

| | | | |
|---|---|---|---|
| C16:1 | mo | Palmitoleic acid | 0.3% |
| C18:0 | st | Stearic acid | 1.5 - 2.5% |
| C18:1 | mo | Oleic acid | 12.5 - 14% |
| C18:2 | pu | Linoleic acid | 72 - 77% |
| C18:3 | pu | Linolenic acid | 0.5% |

## Name: PEACH KERNEL OIL
Botanic Name: *Prunus persica*

### General Information

The Peach tree has been cultivated in China for over two thousand years, where it also grows wild, although it is believed that Persia was the country of origin. Some say that it was the soldiers of Alexander the Great who took the peach to Greece. It is now cultivated in France, other parts of Europe, northern Africa, Iran, Mongolia, and California, and is one of the world's most popular fruit trees. It is regarded as a symbol of revival, youth and fleeting love! According to Chinese legend, whoever eats peaches from the Koudiou mountain will be given eternal life! In ancient times, the Chinese used the peach tree branches to repel evil spirits and disease, and the peach stone was worn around the necks of children and domestic animals as a talisman!

This small tree can reach two to five metres in height, with slender green or reddish branches. The bright pink flowers appear before the leaves in early spring. The fruit appears later in summer, from July to September, and it is large, yellow or red, fleshy and velvety, with a rough stone. The oil is generally cold pressed and commands a premium over its other two relatives, Sweet Almond and Apricot.

In the Middle Ages, peach tree leaves were recommended for epilepsy and worms, and to help with hearing difficulties. The bark and stone were also used to treat various ailments such as headaches, angina, gout, and gland disorders. The milk extracted from crushed peach stones was used in exorcism rites, and divining rods were made from the wood. A nice wine can be made from peaches, so it is very versatile.

## Properties and Uses

A very pale yellow, with the lightest of odours, this oil makes an ideal facial massage oil. I find it is a little richer than its cousins, with a trace more body to its touch. Peach Kernel Oil has moisturising, regenerative and restructuring properties and thus has anti-ageing value. It provides good counter types to natural skin lipids, and so is compatible even with sensitive skins. Its obvious use is in high class anti-wrinkle eye creams for mature skins, lip balms, hand and body lotions, dry skin products, and massage oils – anywhere where a nourishing but relatively light oil is needed.

The oil can be taken internally and, as a monounsaturate with some essential fatty acid, is a beneficial dietary supplement.

### Typical Fatty Acid Profile

| | | | |
|---|---|---|---|
| C16:0 | st | Palmitic acid | 5 - 8% |
| C18:1 | mo | Oleic acid | 55 - 75% |
| C18:2 | pu | Linoleic acid | 15 - 35% |

An unsaponifiable content of 0.5% is average.

# Name: RASPBERRY SEED OIL
## Botanic Name: *Rubus idaeus*

### General Information

Raspberry is known by most people in Northern Europe. It's a berry that along with so many others, such as cloud berry and blackberry, has formed part of the traditional northern diet. It is used for jam and consumed as a dessert. Raspberries also occur in South America. Raspberry grows on the forest edge and in damp glades, although I have seen it deep in the forests of Finland. Raspberry leaves are used for throat infections and the tea is used to relieve spasmolitic cramps and pains.

The oil contains vitamin E and carotenes, and keeps well. The seeds are turned to flour before being cold pressed to yield an orange/yellow oil. The oil has a delicate and attractive odour. Not all Raspberry Seed Oil is produced this way and some may in fact be $CO_2$ extracts rather than a pressed oil. Such extracts have value, but they are very much part of a controlled and standardised extract with exact replicable characteristics.

### Properties and Uses

Raspberry Seed Oil has been in use for some time and it was quite trendy in the 1960's, based on German work. Since then research has taken place in Canada, France, and Finland. All confirm that ellagic acid, a phenolic compound, has some importance and potential in the prevention of some cancers such as that of the prostrate or breast. Raspberry seed is the richest source. The oil also has some sun screening properties against UVB and C. This is combined with good anti-oxidising properties, which will make a positive impact on the skin.

All together, this is a useful addition to the repertoire open to the Aromatherapist. It is a light oil and leaves little stickiness when used for general massage. It may well be used as a carrier where inflammation is present, and for burns. It is astringent and softening, opening up good opportunities to use it as a soft skin toner.

**Typical Fatty Acid Profile**

| | | | |
|---|---|---|---:|
| C16:0 | st | Palmitic acid | 1 – 4% |
| C18:0 | st | Stearic acid | 2% |
| C18:1 | mo | Oleic acid | 10 – 14% |
| C18:2 | pu | Linoleic acid | 50 – 62% |
| C18:3 | pu | Linolenic acid | 21 – 29% |

## Name: RICE BRAN OIL
Botanic Name:  *Oryza sativa*

### General Information

Rice grows in warm and wet areas, and is cultivated in paddy fields, which are flooded when the plant begins to grow. It is mainly cultivated in the Far East and also in Egypt, Italy, and some parts of France and the American conti-nent. It is the most eaten cereal in the world.

This herbaceous annual plant, covered in flat leaves, can reach two metres in height and, when ripe, the seed has a yellowish colour. These seeds and the bran are used in medicine, and the very soft, fine rice flour is often recommended to relieve inflammation as well as historically being the main ingredient of cosmetic face powder! Rice can be roasted and used as a coffee, and is also made into a low-alcohol drink. It is used as starch for laundry, and in water makes a strong glue.

Paddy rice is known to be more nutritious than the potato, but under-goes rigorous treatments (before being eaten by a third of the world), which, sadly, destroys most of the vitamin content.

In Japan the mouse is seen as the friendly creature that, by legend, saved the country from starvation by introducing it. It's a long story but explains why the mouse crops up in so many carvings and pictures in Japan.

## Properties and Uses

Rice Bran Oil is made from the husk or bran as well as the germ of the seeds. It has skin softening, restructuring and moisturising properties and, because of its anti-oxidising virtues, it is a useful ingredient in anti-ageing preparations. The unsaponifiable content is high, 3-4 %, and the key item is the sterol oryzanol. This has functions such as decreasing cholesterol, combating the effects of stress, improving blood circulation, and reducing inflammation.

It is used in hair shampoos for damaged and fine hair; moisturising creams for dry, mature skins, particularly for around the eyes; and lip balms. In the delicate eye area, because of its antioxidant properties combined with its micro circulation stimulating effects, it would be particularly of value to puffy eyes and those with dark circles.

In general use, the palest yellow oil is a medium viscose oil well-suited to massage, both face and body work. The quality is important if the above effects are needed. Highly refined oils will not have the same activity. Oryzanol or ferulic acid is available as a supplement.

### Typical Fatty Acid Profile

| | | | |
|---|---|---|---|
| C16:0 | st | Palmitic acid | 13 - 23% |
| C18:0 | st | Stearic acid | 2 - 3% |
| C18:1 | mo | Oleic acid | 32 - 38% |
| C18:2 | pu | Linoleic acid | 32 - 47% |
| C18:3 | pu | Linolenic acid | 1 - 3% |

Unsaponifiable content of 3 – 4%.

## Name: ROSE HIP SEED OIL
Botanic Name: *Rosa rubiginosa*


### General Information

Rose Hip Seed Oil is one of the most important oils introduced to Aroma-therapy by the Fragrant Earth Company. The Company has done more than any other to draw the attention of, and introduce to professional Aroma-therapists the wealth of materials from Nature. They are world experts on vegetable oils, and small wonder they promoted this oil so much. Rose Hip Oil is obtained from the Rose Hips of a wild rose, which grows mainly in the Andes and the southern part of Chile. The rose grows in thick spiny bushes, with the well-known red hips displayed over winter.

Many know that rose hips are the best source of natural vitamin C. Rose Hip syrup is a standard. Jam and wine can be made from the hips. My wife and I collected many hips for these purposes from the sand dunes of North Devon, England. We soon learned that the tiny seeds are attached to hair like fronds, the basis of itching powder. These hairy fronds can be fatal if breathed in.

Legend tells us that all roses were white until Aphrodite pricked herself whilst tending to her lover, Adonis. Her blood stained the petals red. The red rose remains the symbol of passionate female love and the white the ecstasy of man. The Romans loved roses and indulged in them to an extent we would consider impossible.

The species 'rubiginosa' is so called because of its rust red autumn foliage. Common names include 'Muscat Rose' or 'Rosa Mesquita', 'Sweetbriar' or 'Eglantine'. It closely resembles the Dog Rose of the English hedgerow but its foliage has a sweet smell.

The industry is labour intensive, requiring hand picking. There is a pre-drying stage followed by controlled drying, de-hipping and the removal of irritants, followed by pressing. There is also a solvent extraction in addition to the pressing. A process of winterisation (removing the heavy waxes by refrigeration) is normal to allow the oil to be more workable or user-friendly.

The oil does not have good keeping qualities in its simple form hence the prevalence of refined oils. When buying cold pressed or crude material, make sure it is not rancid.

## Properties and Uses

Clinical trials carried out on Rose Hip Oil have shown that it contains essential nutrients which make it an exceptionally active product in the field of tissue regeneration, thus improving skin texture and reducing scars and skin discolouration. It is the single most effective oil for use as an anti-scarring agent for all types; refractile, hypertrophic, hyperchromic and even against cheloid or aged hardened scar tissue. It is excellent for serious friction burns. For such work it needs to be applied daily over time.

It can be applied directly on to the body or in formulations for the treatment of surgical scars, burns, and marks. Ideal combinations can be made with essential oils and particularly the herbal oil, Centella asiatica.

So many use it for anti-scarring purposes that people tend to forget that this is also one of the best anti-wrinkle oils. It is incorporated into cosmetic products for smoothing out facial lines and wrinkles, slowing down skin ageing process, moisturising and hydrating. It is a rich oil unsuited to massage and a little on the heavy side, making it ideal for rich, nutritive creams, lotions, and cleansers. Using it neat suits many of my clients and patients, but I have seen good results with inclusions as low as 10 %.

### Typical Fatty Acid Profile

| | | | |
|---|---|---|---|
| C16:0 | st | Palmitic acid | 3.6% |
| C18:0 | st | Stearic acid | 2.15% |
| C18:1 | mo | Oleic acid | 15% |
| C18:2 | pu | Linoleic acid | 47.7% |
| C18:3 | pu | Linolenic acid | 28.5% |
| C20:0 | st | Arachidic acid | 0.9% |
| C20:1 | mo | Eicosenoic acid | 0.45% |
| C20:2 | pu | Eicosadienoic acid | 0.15% |
| C22:0 | st | Behenic acid | 0.2% |
| C22:1 | mo | Docosenoic acid | 0.15% |

# Name: SAFFLOWER OIL
## Botanic Name: *Carthamus tinctorius*

### General Information

The Safflower plant has been cultivated since very ancient times in northern Africa, the Middle East and latterly in the Sacramento Valley area of California where it is known as 'American Saffron'. Its seeds have been found even in the oldest of Egyptian tombs and the mummy bandages were dyed with it. Its original Western and Middle Eastern use was as a dye plant, and the common name 'Bastard Saffron' indicates both its colour and its use to adulterate true Saffron. It has an orange and red pigment that is characteristic of the rouge and face powders of women using the traditional cosmetics of Algeria, Tunisia, Libya, and Egypt. It probably originated somewhere in Central Asia. In the East it has always been seen as an oil-producing crop. The oil has been used as a lamp oil.

Another odd fact about the plant's original use is its capacity, by flower and seed, to curdle milk. The enzyme responsible translates fresh milk into one of the many ferments that are quite unknown to Westerners except for yoghurt. The milk and honey of the Bible is more than likely to be sweet and sour! Parrots love the seeds, hence another common name, 'Parrot Seed'.

### Properties and Uses

The oil has never been popular in Aromatherapy, although relatively cheap, light, and easy to use. For economic purposes, it has much to commend it over some of the refined and cheap oils some Aromatherapists, Aestheticians, and Body Workers foist on their unsuspecting clients and patients as 'pure and natural'. Safflower Oil is very rich in essential fatty acids, which are beneficial in many treatments for the skin. This oil is high in polyunsaturated acids, making it attractive as a dietetic where it may well suit those with arteriosclerosis or those prone to thrombosis. It does not keep well, so if used for culinary purposes, make sure the oil is not rancid and use it quickly. It is not a good frying oil.

**Typical Fatty Acid Profile**

| | | | |
|---|---|---|---|
| C16:0 | st | Palmitic acid | 6 – 7% |
| C18:0 | st | Stearic acid | 2 - 3% |
| C18:1 | mo | Oleic acid | 14 - 15% |
| C18:2 | pu | Linoleic acid | 70 – 80% |

# Name: SESAME OIL
Botanic Name: *Sesamum indicum*

## General Information

Can anyone familiar with British Pantomime or The Thousand and One Nights resist starting with the words 'Open Sesame'. The Hebrews, Babylonians, and Egyptians all knew of semsen or simsin. Sesame symbolises immortality and life, hence the use of the name to open caves or tombs. Allotted to Ganesh, the happy elephant god of Hindu mythology, sesame is a lucky talisman to bring money. As Ali Baba knew, the whole world of magic was hidden in this tiniest of seeds.

The Sesame plant has been cultivated from ancient times by the Egyptians and others. These days, it is grown in China, India, Pakistan, Greece, and South America. The nutritious oil is extracted from the seeds of the plant. White seeds, as opposed to black, are favoured by traditional users for producing the best oil. The oil is amazingly stable, indicating its potential uses in skin care and dietetics. A genuine seed oil, it yields over 50 % of its weight in oil. Most oil is hot pressed and refined. Sometimes the seeds are roasted to impart taste. Cold pressed, virgin oil is obtainable, and gives a light yellow oil.

## Properties and Uses

Sesame is a highly desirable oil for aromatherapy practice and one of my favourites. It is good for moisturising and makes a fine massage oil. Sesame is a fine cooking oil, and the seed paste known as 'tahini' is increasingly popular and useful. East Europeans, Greeks, and Turkic people love 'halva', made from sesame seeds and honey. It was one of my first sweets and still remains a favourite. Why take supplements when you can enjoy natural foods.

Sesame blends well with Walnut Oil for a rich, nurturing massage oil. For many years I have suggested that Sesame, added to many blends at 20 % inclusion, will give useful benefit for skin care. High in essential fatty and polyunsaturated acids, this oil contains skin restructuring and emollient properties making it a popular additional ingredient for soaps and detergents too. Its keeping properties revolve around two unusual and specific compounds, sesamine and sesamoline, together with beta sitosterol. So apart from emollience, the integrity of skin structure is reinforced and free radical scavenging activity is present, making this a very practical oil for body and face nourishing creams, masks, and wraps. In addition it has slight hydrophilic properties and so spreads well when used as a straight, but sticky, bath oil.

### Typical Fatty Acid Profile

| | | | |
|---|---|---|---|
| C16:0 | st | Palmitic acid | 8 - 11% |
| C18:0 | st | Stearic acid | 4 - 6% |
| C18:1 | mo | Oleic acid | 37 - 42% |
| C18:2 | pu | Linoleic acid | 30 - 47% |

The unsaponifiable content, at a typical 1.5%, includes natural anti-oxidising sterols.

Name: SHEA BUTTER

Botanic Name: *Butyrospermum parkii*


## General Information

A mystical tree from Africa. Introduced to Europe by the legendary explorer Mungo Park for whom it is named. Like the African women who use it to relax the body and care for the skin, every Aromatherapist should learn to love this noble butter oil. It is used for cooking, and the tree itself gives many benefits to the indigenous peoples including latex, food, and medicine. It is not cut for timber or firewood.

A tree of the wide savannahs, it is particularly associated with Mali and Burkina Faso. The tree can grow to 20 metres and does not reach its full producing capacity for forty years. It produces berries the size of large plums, containing up to three seeds. One tree produces 20 kg of fruit yielding 4 kg of kernels, in turn giving 1.5 kg of butter. The trees are often wild harvested and may have an aura of magic.

There are two quite distinct extraction processes. The first is cold-pressing, thereby preserving all components intact as in traditional use, but it gives low yields and so is higher priced. The second, and by far the most common, is a hexane solvent extraction. The chocolate industry consumes most of the material but it is found in the margarine and other food industries.


## Properties and Uses

Aromatherapists possibly use this butter without realising it. The very best creams and cream bases use it as the first active principle or ingredient. It has tremendous skin softening properties. Students love the texture when I hand it around at lectures. It leaves the hands so soft. The Mali people use it to treat sprains and muscular pain, and its anti-inflammatory properties make it a good base for anti-rheumatic treatments. It is also used as an after-shave balm and as a dry hair lotion. It is even applied to the umbilical chord of the newborn to facilitate healing.

Shea butter, also known as Karité, displays a protective role in screening against UV rays. It contains cinnamic acid, known to give protection. Shea butter also has activity in cell regeneration and capillary micro-circulation, so giving its healing properties for cracks, fissures, and skin ulcers. Anti-elastase characteristics make it useful in the prevention of stretch marks, making the skin suppler.

With an aspect of a thick paste and a colour that may vary from greenish yellow to pale cream, the oil can be applied for massage. You will find that the skin absorbs the oil very greedily and without leaving the fatty residue you would expect. The skin will feel softer and fuller after use. Oil quality varies tremendously by season and variety; 'magnifolia' being judged the best variety. The way the nuts have been handled or collected also has a bearing on the components and results.

If you cannot obtain it, or the right cold pressed quality, look out for it in the better quality creams being sure to check the grades used. The 'cheap' natural companies are likely to use the refined material.

**Typical Fatty Acid Profile**

| C16:0 | st  | Palmitic acid |  3 – 5%  |
|-------|-----|---------------|----------|
| C18:0 | st  | Stearic acid  | 30 – 45% |
| C18:1 | mo  | Oleic acid    | 40 – 45% |
| C18:2 | u   | Linoleic acid |  3 – 9%  |

Unsaponifiables range as high as 8%, which is remarkable compared to other oils. Of the total, Triterpenic alcohols dominate, in particular alpha amyrine and lupeol. In addition, there is a 4 – 7 % sterol content and a good degree of tocopherols.

Name: SOYBEAN OIL
Botanic Name: *Glycine max/Soja hispida*

### General Information

These days soya bean seems to get everywhere as a filler in everything from cakes to sweets. It is a huge crop in the US. Unfortunately, most is subject to Genetic Modification and that would certainly be true of crops and oil coming from China. The Soybean plant is a native of China and is cultivated throughout Asia for its beans, each of which contain 18 to 25% lipids, proteins, vitamins, carbohydrates, trace elements, and some starch. It is the basis of tofu, or bean curd. It has been in domestic use as a food source for at least four thousand years. Perhaps that is where it should have remained, as its oil yield is low, around 15 - 20% depending upon variety, and it is a product of solvent extraction.

### Properties and Uses

Soybean Oil is used for cooking and salad dressings; it's a good dietary product. As a multi-purpose and nutritious crop, soya is heavily promoted. Where would tofu, miso and tempeh be without it and what about the so-called soya milk? Let's not forget soy sauce. Due to its polyunsaturates it turns up as margarine but, in turn, is therefore not good as a frying oil, although a very common cooking oil.

The oil is rich in lecithins and provides a starting material for many products found in natural cosmetics such as dispersants, detergents, and emulsifiers. The oil is used across the whole spectrum of industrial purposes from lamp oil to paint. The residue is the basis of many animal feeds.

It finds little use in topical Aromatherapy, but as it is ubiquitous it is not hard to find on labels in one of its many guises. Make sure it is used for a purpose other than cheapening or bulking a product.

Because it is an emollient, it reinforces the skin's defence barrier and prevents moisture loss. It can be used in nourishing creams, body milks, and face and body moisturising products.

## Typical Fatty Acid Profile

| | | | |
|---|---|---|---|
| C16:0 | st | Palmitic acid | 8 -13% |
| C16:1 | mo | Palmitoleic acid | 0.2% |
| C18:0 | st | Stearic acid | 2 - 5% |
| C18:1 | mo | Oleic acid | 17 - 26% |
| C18:2 | pu | Linoleic acid | 50 - 62% |
| C18:3 | pu | Linolenic acid | 4 - 10% |

0.5 to 1.6% unsaponifiables are present, including tocopherols.

Name: SUNFLOWER OIL

Botanic Name: *Helianthus annuus*

## General Information

Fields of sunflowers are a delight to the eye and form many picturesque backgrounds in Europe from the Ukraine to France. 'The sunflowers' by Van Gogh is a world recognised picture. The Sunflower is actually a native to the Americas and was traditionally cultivated by Native American Indians. Sacred to the Maya and Aztec, the plant has been used for many talismanic protective purposes. The sap of the stem was said to bring wisdom. It was only introduced into Europe in the middle of the 16th Century for decorative purposes, and then used as a food. The seeds are still eaten today just like nuts, and the buds used like artichokes.

The Russians were the first to exploit the properties of Sunflower Oil. Today it is one of the most useful and widely grown edible oil crops. It is so aptly named because the flowers always turn their heads to the sun and because the yellow to orange flowers look so sunny. Most children recognise the plant that, as an annual, reaches for the sky, growing six feet or more in just a few months.

A much-cultivated plant, the varieties yield different qualities of a yellow oil. Some are high in oleic acid and others in linoleic. The seeds yield about 30 % of weight in oil. Processing is as variable as variety, and most is refined. Organically grown and cold pressed material is available.

## Properties and Uses

Sunflower Oil is recognised after Olive as the best oil for cooking. In Eastern Europe it replaces Olive. The cooking oil variety has less linoleic acid than its medicinal or cosmetic companions. Sunflowers have many purposes, from a 'tobacco' to margarine production, from lamp oil to paper making, from hair colorant to soap and detergent manufacture. It is truly one of Nature's most useful plants.

Medicinally, in its heartlands of Eastern Europe the leaves and flowers are used for a variety of chest ailments, especially bronchitis, when mixed with essential oils and herbs. The oil contains inulin, effective in the treatment of asthma, and may well be used as a specific carrier for the essential oil 'Inula', so useful for respiratory problems. The oil is also a well-used folk remedy for rheumatic pain, both in Europe and the Americas.

Herbal oils or macerations commonly use sunflower as their base. It is the premium material for oil solvent extraction. For Calendula, and St. John's Wort, this oil will invariably be used as it is finer than Olive. A good Sunflower Oil is very beneficial in skin care. It resembles human sebum and is a neutral oil in the sense that it mirrors the natural skin lipids. It makes a good oil in which to dilute more expensive materials and because of its easy identifiable organic availability, can be used as a formulation ingredient to boost organic status. As a straight massage oil it is fine, sometimes a little sticky and coarse but satisfactory for slippage and for general massage work. It is infinitely preferable to mineral oil and relatively cheap. Do not confuse oils for body work with cooking oil. With its film forming properties, it can provide good hair conditioning for dry and heat-damaged hair.

For dietary intake why not use it as a dip, condiment, or dressing.

164

**Typical Fatty Acid Profile**

| | | | |
|---|---|---|---|
| C16:0 | st | Palmitic acid | 5 - 8% |
| C16:1 | mo | Palmitoleic acid | 0.1 - 0.4% |
| C18:0 | st | Stearic acid | 4 - 6% |
| C18:1 | mo | Oleic acid | 15 - 25% |
| C18:2 | pu | Linoleic acid | 62 - 70% |
| C18:3 | pu | Linolenic acid | 0.2 - 1.4% |
| C20:0 | st | Arachidic acid | 0.0 - 0.3% |
| C20:1 | mo | Eicosenoic acid | 0.2 – 1.0% |
| C22:0 | st | Behenic acid | 0.5 - 1.1% |

The 1% unsaponifiable content contains campesterol and stigmasterol.

Name: **TAMANU OIL**

Botanic Name: *Calophyllum inophyllum*

## General Information

The Tamanu tree is native to Tropical Asia. It is cultivated in Melanesia and Polynesia, where it is widespread on most of the islands, growing primarily in the coral sands and on the seashore, but sometimes in the valleys inland as long as the ground is moist. Stands are found in the islands of the Indian Ocean and Indonesia, wherever sea drift takes the seed.

The Tamanu tree is two to three metres high and has a thick trunk covered with a rough, black, fissured bark. The Tamanu tree is a good-looking tree with white fragrant flowers similar to linden. It has elegant foliage or leaves, and the name 'Calophyllum' means exactly that. The fruit has a smooth, yellow skin enclosing a layer of pulp, underneath which is a soft nut containing a pale yellow kernel. It looks a little like an apple. 'Tamanu' is the South Seas name, Europeans may know it best as the 'Alexandrian Laurel'.

Legends abound about the tree. It was planted to enclose the marae, the sacred grove. Under the circle's shade, the gods watched the rites of cannibalism. The victim's left eye was placed on a Tamanu leaf as an offering. Victims were hung from the branches. Not exactly a romantic view!

Tamanu is cold pressed from the kernel. The tree has many assets including a greenish resin from the bark called 'calaba balm'. This is used to stop bleeding and as a local anaesthetic. The fruit is pulped and the mass is sometimes used as a healing agent. The whole tree seems to exhibit pain-relieving properties. The Tamanu Oil itself forms in the course of desiccation and is obtained from the kernel. The kernels are sun dried, reducing weight by about a third. As the kernels brown, the distinctive odour forms and the kernels then yield 75 % of their weight in oil. The colour is dark inky green with a strong odour. Refined oil may be a lighter yellow green. In cold temperatures, it will solidify.

## Properties and Uses

Tamanu Oil has healing and protective properties, and has strong analgesic and anti-inflammatory with cicatrising effects. It can be combined with Rose Hip Seed Oil, although generally is used alone or in combination with essential oils. In the South Sea Islands, it is used to alleviate pains due to leprosy, sciatica, and rheumatism, and as a cure for ulcers and bad wounds.

Tamanu Oil is used in the pharmaceutical industry for chapped skin preparations and is also efficient in the treatment of more serious skin problems, such as burns and post-surgical wounds. The oil contains terpenoids and phenolic compounds, including benzoic acid.

Because of its anti-inflammatory, antibiotic or antiseptic properties, industry finds Tamanu Oil an excellent raw material for protective formulations such as soothing creams, lotions and balms; and as after-hair-removal creams, after-sun milks, or for sores and minor sting and bite preparations. Tamanu is not suitable for massage or diet, and should be used as a formulation ingredient and for spot topical applications. Aromatherapists could consider the oil for fissures, cracks, and lesions. Painful joints and muscles should respond well, as may neuralgia. Its anti-inflammatory and pain relief properties indicate its use in shingles. Its use requires care, remembering it will increase local blood supply.

**Typical Fatty Acid Profile**

| C16:0 | st | Palmitic acid | 15% |
|-------|----|--------------|-----|
| C18:0 | st | Stearic acid | 74% |
| C18:1 | mo | Oleic acid | 10% |

The unsaponifiable content includes coumarin derivatives specific to the tree such as calophyllic acid.

Name: WALNUT OIL
Botanic Name: *Juglans regia*

### General Information

The Walnut tree is very tall, big and handsome and is found in all temperate areas throughout Europe, especially France. The USA is the world's largest producer but it is thought to have originated in Persia. The timber makes for fine furniture. The male flowers hang like catkins and the females are gathered on the extremity of the branches. All the flowers are a greenish colour. The large plum-like but green fruit contains the familiar wrinkled nut. The doctrine of signatures suggests walnuts are good for the brain, as the kernel, too, is compressed and wrinkled, looking a little like brains. The leaves give a dark dye and were used as a hair colorant. The dye, juglone, has bactericidal and fungicidal qualities, and so probably contributed to hair hygiene as well. It is a first class culinary nut often used in cakes.

The ancients saw the nut as the food of gods. 'Juglans' is a corruption of 'Jove's glans' or 'Jove's acorn'. It has a sinister reputation and witches gather under it. When early morning mist lingers by a walnut tree, it is said to be the underclothes of the witches!

The cold pressed rich oil is golden, and the refined a lighter hue. The oil is very unsaturated, so its keeping qualities have to be watched. A true oil nut, it gives 50% of its weight in oil. Many qualities of oil are produced including cooking oil made from roasted nuts. Nuts are bleached to 'improve' consumer acceptance, but such nuts have a more bitter taste. Organic produce is available for consumption and Aromatherapy.

**Properties and Uses**

The leaves from the Walnut have a long history of use in skin care and the treatment of skin disorders.

Walnut Oil is used for salad dressings and is well appreciated for its tasty, unique flavour. The nuts make a good dietary supplement especially when fresh, sometimes then referred to as wet walnuts. Pickled walnuts are a delicacy. A fine liqueur and an aperitif are made from walnuts. Attributes include increasing lactation, antianaemic properties, and reduction in blood cholesterol levels. Circulation may be improved.

The oil is exceptionally emollient, helping the skin to retain moisture and to soften. It is my massage oil of choice, particularly as clients and patients love its texture and almost creamy feel and touch. It will be readily seen to tone the skin and presents regenerative and anti-ageing properties. Slippage is good with a medium weight. The oil has enough body to be maintained at the surface, without immediate absorption, making it an ideal massage medium. It can be used in nourishing creams, body milks, and skin moisturising products; but the instability, colour and odour might make a good refined or semi-refined material a better choice than virgin crude organic for formulation ingredient applications.

### Typical Fatty Acid Profile

| C14:0 | st | Myristic acid | 0.1% |
|-------|-----|---------------|------|
| C16:0 | st | Palmitic acid | 6 - 8% |
| C16:1 | mo | Palmitoleic acid | 0.2% |
| C18:0 | st | Stearic acid | 1 - 3% |

| C18:1 | mo | Oleic acid | 14 - 21% |
| C18:2 | pu | Linoleic acid | 54 - 65% |
| C18:3 | pu | Linolenic acid | 9 - 15% |

The unsaponifiable content reaches 1% rich in sitosterols.


Name: WHEAT GERM OIL

Botanic Name: *Triticum sativum*


## General Information

Wheat is a herbaceous cereal plant, cultivated extensively all over the world. The name 'Triticum', to grind, alludes to the plant's role as a main ingredient of flour for bread. It has been cultivated for time immemorial, probably originating as a cultivated plant from wild grasses in the Euphrates basin. Gods have long been associated with the plant, Osiris, Demeter, and Ceres to name a few. Wheat has always symbolised wealth and fertility.

It is an annual plant cultivated all over the world in numerous varieties, hard and soft, winter and summer. Today significant amounts come from Genetically Modified stocks. It has been used for medicinal purposes but it should be thought of mainly as a staple food – bread. The argument over white bread versus brown bread and the value of pastas is too well known to reiterate here. The colour depends upon the milling, the bran, the husk and the germ, brown and yellow can be removed by grinding.

The production of oil from the germ takes a number of forms. There is no cold pressed germ oil. Hot pressing, solvent extraction, and vacuum are common. There is an oil extract, usually sold as the real thing, where the wheat is macerated in another oil, which is taken up by the seed and then the loaded seed is cold pressed. These methods means there are variable values to the oils. Good oil does not come cheap. All the values should be related to the high vitamin E content. The colour varies from a deep orange to yellow.

**Properties and Uses**

Wheat Germ Oil is very high in vitamin E and gives a good proportion of unsaturated fatty acids. Neither should its high content of sterols be over-looked, along with vitamins A and B complex. It is used for salad dressings and in health food products. It is also suitable for the manufacture of capsules and other medical or supplement preparations.

It is often used in Aromatherapy as an antioxidant material to stabilise blends. It should not be relied upon as the vitamin E present will not be enough to do the job. Something is better than nothing though. Look for a specified content in natural vitamin E; 0.2% is likely the best you will find.

The oil is an emollient and is used in nourishing creams, body milks, and face and body moisturising products. The antioxidants present make it a prime candidate for inclusion in restructuring creams and gels, and other products designed for mature or damaged skins. It is unsuitable for massage, being heavy to work with and with a distinct odour.

**Typical Fatty Acid Profile**

| C16:0 | st | Palmitic acid | 14 - 18% |
|-------|-----|---------------|----------|
| C18:0 | st | Stearic acid | 0.5 - 0.6% |
| C18:1 | mo | Oleic acid | 16 - 22% |
| C18:2 | pu | Linoleic acid | 54 - 58% |
| C18:3 | pu | Linolenic acid | 4 - 7% |

Unsaponifiables are present at 3 - 4%. They are particularly rich in sterols, essentially beta sitosterol and campesterol. Lecithin can be found at 2%.

# Herbal Oils

Herbal oils, phytols or macerations are not the same as fixed oils. Some Aromatherapy supply companies mix them but they are not the same thing. They are valuable in Aromatherapy in their own right, and their study is worthwhile.

From reading some books on Aromatherapy, you would think that distillation has been common the world over for millennia. It has not. The commonest way to extract the goodness from a herb was to boil it, make a tea, or make an oil extract. Alcohol and distillation came much later. Even today we still find native people making extracts using lard from goats, even geese, as well as the vegetable butters.

Herbs contain active chemicals. Some of these chemicals can be drawn out, dissolved into a solvent. Solvents might be natural, like oil and water, or manufactured, like glycerine or alcohol. Some are of natural origin, but some come from synthetic manufacture, the commonest being propylene glycol. Different solvents attract different actives. Vitamin C, for example, is soluble in water whilst vitamin E is oil soluble.

In terms of quality, the solvent plays a part. There is a point at which a solvent becomes fully saturated. It cannot accept any more actives, it is full up. So quality is not a matter of volume but of expertise.

Oil extraction methods come in two types, industrial or solar. The latter is the simplest and can be done at home. In all cases the starting material must be the very best, as must the carrier oil or solvent. In the latter case, a good Organic Sunflower would make a good base.

Large glass containers are filled with the chosen herb and then left in the sun, where heat and light help move the actives. The containers are turned regularly and slow extraction takes place over two to three weeks. St. John's Wort and Calendula are two herbs that yield nicely using this method.

Industrially there is the quick method, as well as what we may term the 'proper' method. If a cheap product is required, say for no more use than a label claim on shampoo, the herb is put into a screw expeller that crushes and mashes the herb into the solvent oil. This can result in no more than a 'tainted' oil, certainly not loaded with actives. St. John's Wort manufactured this way might actually be green whereas it should be red!

Some better quality manufactures do use steeping methods and long term maceration, perhaps too under vacuum. The extraction process is slow and the resultant product fully representative of the plants potential in fat-soluble actives. This would include the essential oils present in small quantities in so many plants that are not distilled. Meadowsweet, so useful for its analgesic effects, is an example.

Macerated oils were the commonly used extracts, which included essential oil components from ancient times. These were the medicines of Galen and the unguents of Cleopatra. They are valuable to all Aromatherapists and are ready to use and safe to handle with a little knowledge. Any fatty acid profile would depend upon the solvent oil used, and has little relevance. It is the active content that counts, along with the memory of the plant.

Herbal oils are a world of their own and require study. A good herbal will provide both background and facts. Below are the three I believe essential, and the most commonly used in practice.

## The Key Three Herbal Oils

### Comfrey *Symphytum officinale*
One of the best-known herbal oils and treatments. It had the common name 'knit bone', indicating its use for breaks, sprains, and similar injuries. Used since Roman times, it is quite effective. One of the main active ingredients is allantoin, a recognised anti-inflammatory.

### Marigold *Calendula officinalis*
This is the common or garden Pot Marigold. The oil in the industry is generally called Calendula Oil. It gives excellent results in all sun and after-sun

creams. It occurs in Greek, Indian, and Arabic medicine. It has a nickname, in the trade, of 'Russian penicillin'. It certainly reduces muscle tension and spasm. It is anti-inflammatory, promoting wound healing, and is suitable for treating piles and fissures.

## St. John's Wort *Hypericum perforatum*

The herb has obtained some status for treating depression yet it has been used for anxiety since Roman times. The oil extract for external use is a rich red and can be used to relieve stomach cramps and muscular spasm. It can be used on cuts and bruises but is very specific to burns. After using it, avoid direct sunlight.

# *Testing Oil By Smell and Taste*

Aromatherapists are familiar with reading the label and literature and then making an assessment by smell. They look for vitality – a certain freshness that is difficult to describe and has nothing to do with odour. It's about arousal, stimulation, life. It is the difference between excellence and mundanity.

Modern consumers are occasionally given the rare privilege of sampling a morsel of cheese or a biscuit in supermarket malls. You see people veer away from the vendor as though the proffered item has something wrong with it. We definitely do not want to be sold something. In the past all market food was sold on sampling, quality, and value. We have lost the art of sampling food. Today, price is king – how stupid we have become that we measure the quality of our very being, our food sources, by price.

Packaging and written information have replaced our natural ability to determine goods by taste, touch, and aroma. It is the last thing a supermarket wants you to do. Government is complicit in this, having created a whole industry of Health & Safety that goes way beyond the idea of sensible hygiene. The result – a sterile world of no taste or smell, and a world in which our children's natural immunity has been so suppressed that they keel over at the first bacteria!

Oils too can be appreciated by taste. The British are just getting the hang of dipping bread into oil and actually enjoying the taste. Oil quality can be judged by taste just as Aromatherapists judge essential oil by smell. Remember most of 'taste' is in fact aroma – retro smelling from the act of chewing from the mouth.

First, smell the oil. Does it have any smell? Does it smell like the nut or seed it comes from? This tells you something about the degree of refinement. Does it smell off? If it does, then it *is* off or rancid! Next take a tiny amount to the tongue and lick it around your mouth, savouring it, 'feeling it'. Feel the taste – is it tart, smooth or even oily. You will acquire a data bank of information. You will soon find 'bland' means just that, whatever the price. Is 'bland' indicative of therapy or value? I think not.

Create your own vocabulary or use the International Olive Oil Council terminology that, whilst specific to their product, can be applied across the spectrum of oils.

BITTER – pleasantly sharp maybe due to young produce.

BLAND – having no taste beyond oiliness due to loss of aromatic elements.

BRINE or SALTY- from salted fruits.

BURNT – exactly that, when overheated or cooked.

EARTHY- musty from old or dirty seed or fruit.

FLAT – over refinement.

FRUITY – like fruity wine, a sweet taste and dry odour.

GRASSY – like mown grass, decreases with age.

GREEN – unpleasantly bitter due to poor harvesting and sorting.

HARSH – a feeling of fresh astringency.

METALLIC – sort of hits the teeth. Caused by unsuitable storage containers or machinery.

MUSTY – dry powdery taste or odour due to contamination by yeast and mould.

PUNGENT – striking odour not matched by taste.

OLD – it just feels old, so usually is.

RANCID or OFF – unpleasant odour and sharp taste that seems to fill the
mouth due to oxidation and perhaps age.

ROUGH – the mouth feels that way.

SMOOTH – runs around the palate, licking good!

SWEET – sweet it is not, but neither is it anything else! It tastes fine and
pleasing.

VINEGAR – certain oils may form acetic acid, which spoils the oil.


No doubt you can, like the proverbial wine taster, add your own adjectives in combination with the basics above. I describe Macadamia as smooth with oodles of chocolate and a sweet yumminess that says more. Got the idea?!

# *My Top Twelve Vegetable Oils*

(The list is in no order of value but are the 'must haves' for practicing therapists)

Apricot Kernel

Avocado

Camellia

Hazelnut

Jojoba

Kukui

Macadamia

Raspberry Seed

Rose Hip

Sweet Almond

Sesame

Walnut

# *My Choice of Favourite Massage Oils*
(Add your own essential oils if you really feel you need them. Enjoy.)

For general massage I use **Walnut** for its slippage and nutritive value. For head massage I use Hazel Nut for its diffusive power.

**Monoi** neat as it comes, it's heavenly when warmed! Let it melt on the skin, run its own way, and breathe the aroma.

**Walnut Oil** at 50%, **Sweet Almond** at 30%, and **Hazelnut** 20%. Smooth and diffusing for relaxation.

**Jojoba** at 10%, **Kukui** at 30%, **Rose Hip Seed** at 10%, and **Apricot Kernel** 50%. A readily absorbed nutritive facial oil for dry, sensitive, and mature skin.

**Sesame** at 40%, **Calendula** at 30%, **Sunflower** at 10%, and **Argan** at 20%. A good oil to keep your tan, and for after-sun.

**Passion Flower seed** at 30%, **Kukui** at 10%, **Macadamia** at 10%, **Peach Kernel** at 30%, and **Camellia** at 20%. Luxury, expensive, fine, regenerative, and a silk touch for the skin. A joy to use too!

**Rose Hip** at 50%, **Wheatgerm** at 10%, **St. John's Wort** at 5%, **Borage** at 20%, and **Jojoba** at 15%. A penetrating healing oil for all damaged skin.

# Bibliography

Ann Charlotte Andersson, *Functional Lipids for Cosmetic Applications*, Sweden, Karlshamns AB.

D. Boskou, *Olive Oil Milling & Quality*, Greece, Aristotle University.

Jean Bruneton, *Pharmacognosy Phytochemistry Medicinal Plants,* Lavoisier.

Susan Miller Cavitch, *The Soapmakers Companion,* Pownal, Vermont, Storey Books.

T. Chalmers, *The Production and Treatment of Vegetable Oils*, Constable & Co.

Anne Dolamore, *The Essential Olive Oil Companion*, Grub Street, 1999.

Liz Earle, *Vital Oils*, London, Ebury Press, 1991.

U. Erasmus, *Fats that Heal, Fats that Kill,* Alive Books, 1993.

John Finnegan, *The Facts about Fats*, Celestial Arts, 1993.

R. B. Gennis, *Biomembranes Molecular Structures and Functions*, Germany, Springer-Verlag.

Werner Heimann, *Fundamentals of Food Chemistry,* Chichester, Ellis Horwood Ltd.

Patrick Holford, *The Optimum Nutrition Bible*, London, Piatkus, 1997.

Leslie Kenton, *Ageless Ageing*, London, Century Publishing, 1985.

M.Konlee, *How To Reverse Immune Dysfunction*, Keep Hope Alive Publishing.

DiaSouss Gmbh, Munich, Product Information.

P. O. Kwiterovich, *Beyond Cholesterol*, USA, John Hopkins University Press, 1989.

R. Mabey, *The New Age Herbalist*, New York, Macmillan, 1988.


W.N. Marmer, *Animal Fats: World Production, Markets, Uses, and Research*, USA.

Leonard Mervyn, *The Dictionary of Vitamins,* Wellingborough, Thorsons Publishers, Ltd, 1984.

B. Thomas, *Manual of Dietetic Practice,* UK, Blackwell Science, 2001.

Robert Tisserand, *The Art of Aromatherapy*, Saffron Walden, The C.W. Daniel Co. Ltd, 1977.

Peter Tompkins & Christopher Bird, *The Secret Life of Plants*, USA, Harper & Row Inc., 1973.

Carol Turkington and Jeffrey Dover, M.D., *Skin Deep*, New York, Facts on File, Inc., 1998.

R. Wysong, *Lipid Nutrition,* Inquiry Press.

*The New Oxford Book of Food Plants*, Oxford University Press, 1997.

The Chemistry of Glycerides. Unilever.

Vegetable Oils and Fats. Unilever.

*Encyclopedia of Common Natural Ingredients*, 2nd edn, USA, Leung & Foster, Wiley Interscience, 1995.

*The Ecologist*, Richmond.

*Living Earth, The Magazine of the Soil Association*, Bristol.

Les Ami des Ingredients, Paris.

# Resources

**Education**

Essentials for Health, Church Lane, London E11 1HG.

Fragrant Studies International Ltd., Orchard Court, 3A Magdalene St., Glastonbury, Somerset BA6 9EW.

Institute of Traditional Herbal Medicine & Aromatherapy, 12, Prentices Lane, Woodbridge, Suffolk IP12 4LF.

**Essential Oils & Aromatherapy**

The Fragrant Earth Co.Ltd, Orchard Court, Magdalene St., Glastonbury, Somerset, BA6 9EW.

Primavera Life, Am Fichstenholz 5, D 87477, Sulzberg, Germany.

Quinessence Aromatherapy, Forest Court, Linden Way, Coalville, Leicester, LE67 3JY

Lab Sanoflor S.A., Quartier les Fonts, 26400 Gigors et Lozeron, France.

# Index

*Personal notes*

*Personal notes*

*Personal notes*

*Personal notes*